MODERN
SIGNAL
HANDB

G000123430

STANLEY HALL

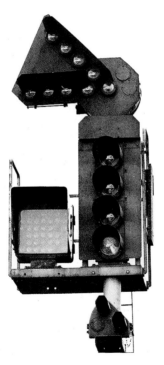

Ian Allan
PUBLISHING

Revised Third
Edition

First published 1992 as *BR Signalling Handbook*
Second edition 1996, Reprinted 2000, Third edition 2001
Revised Third edition 2005

ISBN 0 7110 3143 6

© Stanley Hall 2005

Published by Ian Allan Publishing

an imprint of Ian Allan Publishing Ltd, Hersham, Surrey KT12 4RG.
Printed by Ian Allan Printing Ltd, Hersham, Surrey KT12 4RG.

Code: 0510/C

Visit the Ian Allan Publishing website at www.ianallanpublishing.com

Above: **Ground frame at Fort William. See Chapter 16.** *D. C. Hall*

Title page: **Modern signal head, showing from top to bottom: 1. Route indicator for main aspect (positions 1 and 2); 2. Four-aspect running signal; 3. Theatre-type route indicator; 4. Position light signal.** *IAL*

Front cover: **Class 221, a Super-Voyager bound for Euston is seen departing Holyhead. See page 5 for 'Ensuring Tilting Train Safety'.** *Brian Morrison*

Back cover: **Fibre optic banner repeating signals at Waterloo International.** *Brian Morrison*

Preface

Preface to the First Edition

Despite the apparent simplicity of the lineside signals, the British railway signalling system is a matter of considerable complexity, which is sometimes puzzling even to the professional railwayman and is certainly a source of mystery to most laymen.

This book sets out to remedy that problem. It is written in terms which the author hopes will be clearly intelligible to the layman without being boring to the railwayman. It describes the signals and their various indications, together with the systems of which they are the visual part. And it is an operator's handbook, not a technical manual.

The book is not an official British Rail document, but it embodies BR's Rules, Regulations and Principles, and has been written with BR's co-operation and help. The author wishes to acknowledge his debt to BR for their generous assistance.

Preface to the Second Edition

Four years have elapsed since the first edition was published, and in view of changes in rules and procedures during that time the opportunity has been taken to update the text and to include new material, again with help from British Rail, and also from Railtrack. The author, who was the British Railways Board's Signalling and Safety Officer, gratefully acknowledges that help.

Preface to the Third Edition

Five years have elapsed since the second edition was published and during that time there have been many changes to the Rules, Regulations and Train Signalling Instructions. In addition, there have been technical developments in train protection systems and radio. Opportunity has been taken to update the complete text incorporating all the changes up to and including those of June 2001, and to include completely new chapters on the Train Protection and Warning System, the European Rail Traffic Management System, and signals passed at danger without authority. This handbook is not an official Railtrack document, but it has been written with the company's generous help and encouragement. The author is also indebted to three readers who have made valuable contributions from their particular sphere of knowledge and experience: Geoff Curl, a signaller, Chris Hall, an HMRI Principal Inspector, and Peter van der Mark, a Great Western Trains HST driver. The author gratefully acknowledges his debt to all four parties.

Contents

Right: The transition stage at Nuneaton Trent Valley. Semaphore gantries are being replaced by colour light signals. This photograph enables comparison to be made between colour light and semaphore junction indications. (See Chapter 9.) *IAL*

Preface		2
Part 1	1. Historical Development of Signalling (1)	7
	2. Historical Development of Signalling (2)	9
Part 2	3. Colour Light Signals — Their Meaning	14
	The Sequence of signals. Aspects. Shunting Signals. Position Light Signals.	
	4. Colour Light Signals — Main Aspects. How They are Operated in Colour Light Areas	16
	Controlled and Automatic Signals. Automatic and Emergency Control Buttons. Emergency Replacement Switches. Track Circuit Operating Clips. How Signals go to Red. How Signals are Cleared from Red.	
	5. Colour Light Signals in Colour Light Areas — The Choice of Type, Location and Spacing	18
	Two-, Three- and Four-aspect Signals. Braking Distances. Controlled and Automatic Signals. The Location of Signals.	
	6. Detecting the Presence of a Train by Track Circuits or Axle Counters	21
	The Overlap. Terminal and Bay Platform Lines.	
	7. Junction Signalling in Colour Light Areas	24
	Approach Control and Release of the Junction Signal. Flashing Yellows. Splitting Distants. Approach Locking of Points. Flank Protection.	
	8. Inside a Modern Power Signalbox	28
	Layout of Panel. Method of Operation. Route-setting. Track Circuit Indications. Combined or Separate Panels. Train Descriptions. Information and Miscellaneous Controls. 'Train Ready to Start' Buttons. Visual Display Units.	
	9. Colour Light Signalling — Miscellaneous	31
	Passenger Permissive Signalling. Lamp Proving. Numbering of Colour Light Signals. Remote Control Standby Arrangements. Signals from Sidings to Running Lines. Colour Light Signals not in Use. Delayed Yellow Operation.	
	10. Colour Light Areas — Emergencies	32
	Complete Failure of Signalling Apparatus. Track Circuit Irregularities. Examination of Line. Suspected Track Defects. Suspected Damage to Track or Structures. Broken Rails in Continuously Welded Track.	

Part 3 **11. The Absolute Block System of Signalling** 35
Explanation of the System. Offering and Accepting Trains. Bell Codes and Train Classification. 'Welwyn' Controls. Sykes and Rotary Block Systems. Train Regulation.

12. Semaphore Signals — What They Mean 37
Distant and Stop Signals. Subsidiary Signals. Junction Stop Signals. Banner Repeating Signals. Shunting Signals.

13: Absolute Block Lines — Arrangement of Signals and Track Circuits at Stations and Junctions. Locking and Controls 40
Conventional Layouts at Stations and Junctions. Sequential Locking. 'Home Normal' Contact. Distant Arm Proving. Use of Colour Light Signals. Safety at Points.

14. Absolute Block Lines — Working of Semaphore Signals and the Acceptance of Trains 45
Acceptance Arrangements. Acceptance During Fog and Falling Snow. Restricted Acceptance. Working of Signals at Converging Junctions. 'Train Out of Section' Signal. Working of Signals when the Train is not accepted by the Signalman in Advance. Replacing Signals to Danger or Caution. Working of Signals at Diverging Junctions. Working During Fog or Falling Snow.

15. Absolute Block Lines — Inside the Signalbox. Equipment to Help the Signalman 48
The Lever Frame. The Block Shelf. Block Indicators. Bells. Repeaters. Releases. Block Switch. Flags, Lamps and Detonators. Clock. Train Register Book.

16. Intermediate Block Sections, Automatic Sections, Station Working, Ground Frames 50
Description of Systems.

17. How Emergencies are Dealt With on Absolute Block Lines 51
An Obstruction on the Line. Stopping a Train for Examination. Train in Section for an Unusually Long Time. Train Passing Without a Tail Lamp. Protection of the Line. Dealing with a Train which has Broken Down in Section. Examination of the Line. Failure of the Block Signalling Equipment.

Part 4 **18. The Driver, the Guard and the Signals** 55
Observance of Signals. Doubt as to Signal Aspect. Being Authorised to Pass a Signal at Danger. Train Detained at a Signal at Danger. Failure of Telephone at a Signal.

19. The BR Standard Automatic Warning System of Train Control, Known as AWS 57
Description of the System. Track and Locomotive Equipment. Method of Operation. AWS Gaps. Failures and Irregularities. AWS Isolation.

20. Automatic Train Protection 59
Track and Train Equipment and Method of Operation.

21. The Train Protection and Warning System (TPWS) 62
TPWS. Track Equipment. The Overspeed Sensor. The Train Stop. Options for Development.

22. The European Rail Traffic Management System (ERTMS) 63
ERTMS. ETCS Variants. ETCS Level 1. ETCS Level 2. ETCS Level 3.

23. Platform Starting Signals — Precautions 61
Wrongly Passed at Danger. Method of Assessment of Risk. Special Precautions. Driver's Reminder Appliance.

24. Signals Passed at Danger Without Authority (SPADs) 64
SPAD Indicators. Signal Sighting. Signal Sighting Committee. The Signaller's Actions.

Part 5 **25. Working of Single Lines** 66
The Electric Token Block System. The Tokenless Block system. One-train Working. The 'No Signaller' Token System. Failures of Equipment. The Radio Electronic Token Block (RETB) System.

Part 6   **26. Level Crossings — Manually Operated with Gates or Barriers**   **71**
Number in Use. Gates Operated by a Signalman on Site. Gates Operated by a Crossing Keeper on Site. Barriers Operated on Site (MCB). Barriers Operated Remotely and Supervised by CCTV.

27. Automatic Level Crossings   **72**
Number in Use. Automatic Half-barrier Crossings (AHB). Automatic Barrier or Automatic Open Crossings Locally Monitored (ABCL) and (AOCL). Wrong Direction Rail Movements (AHB-X etc).

28. Other Level Crossings   **76**
Open Crossings. Gates or Barriers Operated by Public or Traincrew. Miniature Warning Lights. Telephone Provision.

Part 7   **29. Hot Axlebox Detectors**   **78**
Description and Method of Operation.

30. Permanent Speed Restrictions   **79**
Lineside Warning Signs and Arrangements.

31. Temporary Speed Restrictions   **80**
Lineside Warning Signs and Arrangements. Method of Dealing with Failures of Equipment. Emergency Temporary Speed Restrictions (ESRs).

Part 8   **32. Train Radio Systems**   **83**
Cab Secure Radio. The National Radio Network. Use of Radio by Signaller in an Emergency. The Emergency Call Procedure. Global System for Mobile Communication — Railways (GSM-R).

Part 9   **33. Engineering Operations on the Line**   **85**
Protection when Line Unsafe. Protection not under Absolute Possession. Protection under Absolute Possession.

Part 10   **34. Channel Tunnel Signalling**   **88**

Part 11   **35. Future Developments**   **89**

Glossary of Technical Terms and Abbreviations   **93**

Ensuring Trains Tilt Safely

On the West Coast Main Line, tilting trains (Class 390 Pendolinos and class 221 Voyagers) have been authorised to run at speeds above the normal maximum permissible speeds allowed for non-tilting trains, except at large stations and on the slow lines. These speeds are referred to as 'Enhanced Permissible Speeds' (EPS) and are designated by special lineside speed signage. Trains must not be allowed to tilt in areas where clearances are tight or be driven too fast causing a possible risk of derailment or even overturning. A new protection system was therefore devised and supplied by Alstom known as the 'Tilt Authorisation and Supervision System' or TASS. Such a system is not required elsewhere in Europe where tilting trains run because of the more generous loading gauge in those countries.

TASS is based on a simplified version of the European Train Control System (ETCS), and the equipment on the trains (a vital computer operating on a two out of three majority voting system) is installed in the space provided for the ETCS equipment. Trackside equipment consists of freestanding 'Eurobalises' requiring no power supply located in the four-foot about every 5 km. These are programmed as required with information about the speed profile of the route ahead and whether or not the train is authorised to tilt. A tilting train picks up this data as it passes over a balise, and this is continually updated as the train passes over successive balises.

TASS should be invisible to a driver under normal circumstances and will only intervene to apply the brakes and slow the train if the driver exceeds the EPS.

Above: The operating floor of Aberdeen South signalbox, which closed over 20 years ago. *J. H. Edser*

Below: A splendid array of semaphore signals on a gantry at Preston, in use until replaced by Preston power signalbox in 1974. *J. H. Edser*

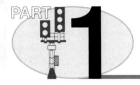

1. Historical Development of Signalling (1)

If trains always ran on time and never broke down there would be little need for a signalling system. The timetable itself could be devised in such a manner that the trains would always be a safe distance apart. This was the philosophy in the early days of railways and worked quite well so long as trains were few and speeds were low, and even though breakdowns were frequent, the guards had time to go back along the line showing a red flag or lamp to warn the driver of the next train about the obstruction in front of him.

However, as the railway age developed and trains became both faster and more frequent, the need for some system of keeping them apart, of preventing them from crashing into each other, quickly became apparent. The first signalling methods were based on a time-interval philosophy. Trains were not allowed to leave or pass a station until a pre-determined time had elapsed since the previous train had left, and the necessary instructions given to the driver in one of two ways — either by hand signal or by fixed signal. Hand signals were given by a policeman appointed for the purpose by the Railway Company and he gave his message to the driver by holding his arms in various positions. At some stations wooden posts were erected, bearing various forms of movable equipment which could be operated by the policeman to give the various messages. These wooden post signals became known as fixed signals because they were literally fixed in the ground in a pre-determined position. The first semaphore signal was erected by the South Eastern Railway at New Cross in 1841. Today's trains are still controlled by fixed signals, although shunting movements are dealt with by both fixed and hand signals.

The time-interval signalling system had fundamental shortcomings. As traffic levels grew it became necessary to run trains at more frequent intervals and if a train broke down, the guard had little time to run back showing his danger signal. A more serious problem arose when a train proceeded slowly for any reason and was thus in danger of being run into in the rear by a following faster train, a danger made more real by the primitive braking systems in use. This type of collision became known as an overtaking accident, with a meaning quite different from its use when applied to road traffic today.

It soon became clear that a much greater standard of safety could be achieved if a train was not allowed to leave a station until it was known that the previous train had arrived safely at the next station, and fortuitously a means had just been devised of allowing this to be done

— the electric telegraph. This equipment began to be installed in the 1840s and led to the development of what became known as the absolute block system, based on the principle that safety could be achieved if the line were to be divided into a series of sections (or blocks), with a policeman (or signalman as he was becoming known) at the end of each section, and with no train being allowed to enter the section until the previous train had left it. This principle was described in the following terms — 'The object of Absolute Block signalling is to prevent more than one train being in a block section on the same line at the same time.'

The term 'absolute' refers to the absolute prohibition of there being more than one train in a block section at the same time. The term 'block' then began to take on a more general meaning, to embrace any signalling system worked by electric telegraph between signalmen in adjacent signalboxes, and is still in use today to describe the system employed in the most up-to-date signalled areas, called 'track circuit block'.

The early fixed signals were operated from the foot of the signalpost but it was soon realised that it would be more efficient if signals could be operated from a distance by the pulling of a wire, and it became the practice to concentrate the operation of signals (and subsequently points) in one place, which became known as a signalbox. It then became possible to interlock the levers working the points and signals so that signals conflicting with the routes which had been set could not be given to a driver; the first interlocking installation was at Bricklayers Arms, South Eastern Railway in 1843.

The essentials of a safe and efficient signalling system were now in place:

1. The concentration of control of points and signals in a signalbox
2. The interlocking of points and signals
3. Electric telegraphic communication between adjacent signalboxes
4. The absolute block signalling system and the regulations for its operation.

The absolute block system was installed throughout Britain during the second half of the 19th century (its use on lines used by passenger trains was enforced by the Regulation of Railways Act 1889) and it was gradually refined by the adoption of a variety of technical measures designed mainly to overcome the problem of human error

Left: **Hull Paragon power signalbox, operated by individual thumb switches — the One-Control Switch (OCS) system. When brought into service on 23 April 1938 it was the world's largest route relay interlocking system.** *IAL*

on the part of signalmen. Human error is one of those phrases which over the years has acquired a special meaning in railway parlance. It covers unconscious or unwitting acts, such as a lack of attention or concentration, impulsive but erroneous reactions, errors committed under pressure, and just plain forgetfulness. It recognises the fact that human beings are not infallible, and if the travelling public is to be safeguarded against the possibly calamitous effects of human error on the part of signalmen, it would be advantageous to adopt all the safeguards that the advances in science and technology can provide. These advances were almost always won the hard way, as a result of lessons learned from accidents, and the learning process continued at least until World War 2, but it was difficult to justify the cost of installing the complete range of safeguards at every signalbox, therefore busier signalboxes were better protected than those which were quieter and situated on less important routes.

The braking systems in use on trains during most of the 19th century were primitive and inadequate and, as trains became faster and heavier, drivers found it increasingly difficult to stop safely if the signals were against them (ie at danger). An auxiliary signal was therefore devised, situated several hundred yards before a stop signal, in order to give the driver prior warning of the need to stop if a signal was at danger. This auxiliary signal became known by the term 'distant signal' and originally drivers were expected to stop at it if it was at danger, but the impracticality of this was eventually recognised and the distant signal became regarded as a warning or caution signal, giving the driver prior indication of the state of the stop signal ahead.

Many accidents occurred because drivers found themselves unable to stop in time at a stop signal showing danger, even after having been warned by the distant signal, and they ran past it into collision with a train or vehicles standing just beyond the station signal.

To avoid such collisions, the notion of a safety overlap was adopted, set at a quarter of a mile, and henceforth the signalman did not send the 'train out of section' message to his colleague at the previous signalbox until the rear of the train had passed such a distance beyond the stop signal. This safety overlap became known as the 'quarter of a mile clearance', and the far end of the overlap became known as the 'clearing point'.

The use of the quarter of a mile clearance was unduly restrictive at some places, and a regulation was devised, universally known as Regulation 5 (because it was the fifth regulation in the signalling regulations book), which authorised the signalman at specified locations to allow a train to proceed towards his signalbox from the previous one, with a train or vehicles occupying his quarter of a mile clearance. The driver was advised, by fixed or hand signal, or verbally, that he was being allowed to proceed under the 'Warning Arrangement' (Reg 5), and he was expected to approach the next signalbox cautiously. This regulation originally applied to both passenger and freight trains, but in later years its use was confined to freight trains.

The use of the absolute block system was confined mainly to double and multiple track lines used by passenger trains. So far as lines used exclusively by goods trains were concerned, a system known as permissive block came into use, which allowed more than one train to be in a block section at the same time. There were no safety overlaps, and the driver of a train being admitted to a section of line still occupied by the previous train was advised of the fact by the use of signals or verbally. He was expected to travel sufficiently slowly to be able to stop safely if he caught up with the train in front. Lower standards of safety were accepted in the operation of freight trains than with passenger trains. Permissive block for passenger trains was often introduced at larger passenger stations to enable a train to enter a platform line already occupied by another train, but such movements were made at low speed and over short distances and were therefore reasonably safe.

The development of signalling on single lines had progressed in a similar manner to that on double lines. At first there had been no system other than the timetable, then the electric telegraph came into use for passing messages regulating the passage of trains over single lines between stations. Misunderstandings led to several accidents, and the electric telegraph system was refined by adapting it to control the issue of tokens (or train staffs) which were handed to drivers and gave them authority to enter the single line section. The tokens were contained in token machines kept in each signalbox or station, and the machines at each end of a section were electrically interlocked with each other so that only one token for a section could be out at any one time. Fixed signals were also used and the system became known as the Electric Token Block system.

A system sometimes used on quieter single lines was known as the 'Staff and Ticket' system. A box of tickets was kept in each signalbox or station and could only be unlocked by a key on the end of the staff (a wooden or metal rod). There was only one staff for each section and trains could only be admitted to a single line section from the end where the staff lay. If a train was to be followed by another one, the driver of the first train was given a ticket and shown the staff. The driver of the last train through the section in one direction was given the staff. It was a cheap and simple system, but could lead to delays if the staff happened to be at the wrong end of the section.

On single lines used by only one train, such as short dead-end branches, a very simple system came into use, known as 'One Engine in Steam'. A single line staff, usually a wooden or metal rod, engraved with the name of the branch, was the driver's authority to enter the single line, and as there was only one such staff in existence, safety was assured.

By the end of the 19th century British railway signalling had evolved into a potentially very safe system, and henceforth its development was to be in a different direction. At that time, the railways were very busy indeed and much thought began to be directed towards ways of improving efficiency and reducing costs. The number of signalboxes needed was determined partly by the distance over which a signalman could operate points (finally set at 350yd but less at that time), partly by the workload, and partly by the size of the area which he could control visually. One of the problems which existed in busy areas was the large number of signalboxes required in the conditions then existing. In such circumstances it was very difficult to keep signalmen fully informed of the nature and timing of train movements approaching them so that they could make the best decisions regarding the priority to be afforded to any particular movement. Also, there was frequently insufficient time to enable signalmen to consult one another regarding proposed movements, and the overall result was unnecessary delay to trains on the one hand and wasted line or platform capacity on the other.

Fortunately, as had happened previously, a technical solution was available — the application of electric or pneumatic power to the operation of points and signals — and several large power-operated signalboxes came into use in the few years before World War 1. The first electro-pneumatic installation was at Bishopsgate, Great Eastern Railway, in 1898, and in 1900 the London & North Western Railway installed an all-electric signalbox at Crewe. Whilst the absolute block system was still used, it had to be considerably modified at large stations. In other areas the use of power-operated points and track circuits (an electrically-operated train detection device) enabled two or three signalboxes to be combined into one, but the cost of such schemes limited their application. Track circuits were first successfully used in Britain in1894 in Gas Works Tunnel, outside King's Cross.

Developments between the wars consisted mainly of the further application of existing safety devices and economy measures, but the birth of modern signalling, based on continuous track-circuiting, multiple-aspect colour light signals, and route-setting of points and signals by a single switch, with the interlocking being achieved by electrical relays, belongs to that period, and its development forms our second chapter.

2. Historical Development of Signalling (2)

The landmarks in the development of signalling which we considered in the previous chapter might be briefly stated as:

1. The concentration in one place (the signalbox) of the operation of all the points and signals in an area, and their interlocking.

2. The use of various block signalling systems.

3. The application of power (electrical, pneumatic or hydraulic) to the operation of points and signals, enabling more concentration to take place.

4. The invention of the track circuit, which detects the presence of a train.

In this chapter we take our story forward to the very latest signalboxes, known as Integrated Electronic Control Centres, but they have their genesis on the East Coast main line at Thirsk and Northallerton where, shortly before World War 2, the LNER introduced a new system known as route-relay interlocking, in which the interlocking between points and signals was achieved by electrical relays, and which allowed the signalman to set the points and clear the signal for the desired route merely by turning a switch. On open stretches of line between stations and junctions the signals worked automatically, turning to red (danger) as soon as a train passed them, then to yellow (caution) and two yellows

(preliminary caution), and finally to green as the train went on its way and passed further signals. Three-aspect colour light signals had first been installed between Marylebone and Neasden in 1923 and, in a subsequent development to allow trains to operate at closer headways, four-aspect colour light signals were introduced in 1926 between Holborn Viaduct and Elephant & Castle, on the Southern Railway.

The Thirsk and Northallerton schemes allowed signalmen to control a far greater area, much of it beyond the signaller's view, than previously, and in order that he should know what was going on in those areas out of sight he was provided with a large panel giving a geographical representation of the track layout and signals etc in his area. In the Northallerton signalbox, a series of white electric lights on the panel showed which way the routes were set, also the location of trains (by red lights), and whether signals had been cleared for trains to proceed. The signalman had to remember which trains they were so that he could set the correct route, and give the appropriate priority at junctions. As the areas controlled from one signalbox became larger or more complex, a system of showing a train's identity (or, in railway terms, description) on indicators in the signalbox was devised. These indicators were called, appropriately, train describers.

Signalboxes of the Thirsk/Northallerton type were known as route-setting or one control switch (OCS) installations, because there was one route or control switch for each route at a junction. A refinement of the OCS method has been the NX system, first introduced at Brunswick near Liverpool in 1937.

The letters NX stand for entrance-exit, in which a route is set by pressing a button or turning a switch at the start of (or entrance to) a route and pressing another button at the end of (or exit from) that route. This simplified the signalman's operating equipment and enabled the operating push-buttons (or switches) to be incorporated on the panel itself, leading to the very large combined control and indications panels that were developed from about 1960 onwards. These large panels

required the signalman to walk to and fro to operate the push-buttons, and in some signalboxes the panel functions were split so that the signalman could sit and operate the push-buttons on a console in the form of a miniature replica panel, with all the signal, route, track circuit, etc indications being shown on a larger, separate panel.

In these later installations the train descriptions are shown on the panel by train identity number, in a position corresponding to the actual location of the train on the track. All trains have a four-digit identity number, ie 1A20, the first digit being the class of train (class 1 is an express passenger train), the second digit the route or destination area (eg A=East Coast main line), and the third and fourth digits, the serial number of the train or service. The train description (TD) number is shown on the indications panel next to the signal which the train is approaching, and as the train passes that signal and proceeds towards the next one the TD number automatically steps forwards to be displayed in the next signal section.

These very large signalboxes became standardised during the 1960s and 1970s and now control most main lines and large stations. Technically there is no limit to the area that can be supervised and controlled from one signalbox, and natural development has resulted in some very large installations indeed such as London Bridge and Victoria, each employing many signallers per shift. The name 'signalbox' was felt to be inappropriate for modern installations and they became 'signalling centres', although the designation 'power signalbox', or PSB for short, is still in common use.

In most large signalboxes, the interlocking apparatus controls only those points and signals within the immediate vicinity. The interlocking of points and signals which are further away is usually dealt with in outlying installations, housed in buildings known as remote interlockings, each one dealing with a station or junction area. Communication between the main signalbox and the remote interlockings is by cable, either housed in concrete troughing at the lineside or buried at a shallow depth.

The basis of all power signalling installations is the track circuit, a simple piece of equipment which feeds a weak electric current through a section of track electrically insulated from the adjoining sections. When the wheels of a train pass on to the section of track concerned they short-circuit the current, causing a relay to operate which in turn controls other operations, eg placing signals to danger, locking points, transferring train descriptions on the signalman's panel from signal to signal, etc. All the running lines (ie all lines other than sidings) are track-circuited throughout their length, and signals are erected at conventional intervals, based upon the distance a train needs to stop from full speed. Each signal is capable of showing a red light, a yellow light or a green light. In busy areas, or on busy high speed lines, signals can also display two yellow lights as a preliminary caution.

Track circuits have reached the limit of their technical development and are prone to right-side failure from a number of causes. This puts signals to danger and causes delay. More use is now being made of axle counters, especially in areas where track circuits are particularly prone to failure, eg in wet tunnels and on stretches of line affected by salt water spray. Axle counting equipment counts the number of axles on a train passing over into a section of line and stores the number in a memory. Similar equipment at the far end of the section counts them out of the section. If the two counts agree, the section is considered clear, allowing the signal protecting the section to show a proceed aspect again.

The most recent major development has been the Integrated Electronic Control Centre (IECC), brought about by changes in traffic patterns and technology. The pattern of train services today is much more stable and repetitive than previously and certainly more predictable. Passenger train timetables are now generally based on an even interval, the pattern being repeated each hour. Cancellations, special trains and other deviations from plan are relatively infrequent. Freight trains are not frequently seen on many routes.

An IECC is likely to contain the following features, which distinguish it from the previous generation of power signalboxes:

1. A stable and predictable train service pattern, which can be entered into a computer.
2. Automatic Route Setting (ARS), by means of which the route at a junction is selected by the computer-based on the train description number of an approaching train and a certain amount of priority logic, previously programmed. This relieves the signaller of repetitive tasks.
3. Computer-driven train describer apparatus, which operates the signaller's train describers, and acts as an information base for the dissemination of train running information, public address announcements, the operation of train departure indicators, etc, and for record purposes.

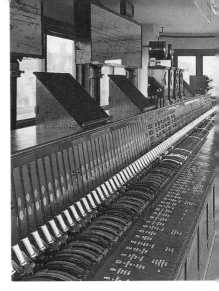

Above: **Miniature lever frame at Woking, 1937.** *IAL*

4. Several visual display units (VDUs), which replace the signaller's operating/indications panel, and require much less space.
5. A change in the method by which the signaller operates points and signals. Instead of using push-buttons he enters his commands either by keyboard or tracker-ball.
6. The interlocking between points and signals, instead of being carried out by banks of electric relays, is dealt with by a computer software program in conjunction with solid-state equipment. This requires much less space, hence the IECC can be housed in a much smaller building than a 1960s/1970s power signalbox.

All communication with trains and all actions in an IECC and in most modern power signalboxes are recorded and stored for later investigation if necessary.

The role of the signaller in an IECC contrasts markedly with that of his colleague in a traditional manually-operated signalbox. In an IECC the signaller controls train movements over a very large area, and he is able to do this because:

1. He can enter his commands quickly and easily.
2. Automatic Route Setting lightens his workload.
3. The visual information of trains, their description and disposition, which is readily available, enables him to determine priorities and make train regulating decisions quickly and to the best advantage.

train in a single line section at the same time was replaced by a system of sequential track circuit occupation and clearance to prove that a train had passed through a section before a further train could be admitted from either end.

Economic necessity led to the development of the most recent method of working single lines — the radio electronic token block system (RETB). It achieves its economy by eliminating the need for intermediate signalboxes and lineside cabling, as all train movements are controlled by radio from a central point. RETB is based in principle on the well-tried electric token block system, the differences being:

1. Instead of the signaller handing the driver a physical token, an electronic 'token' is issued to the driver by radio signal, and appears on an instrument in his driving cab, the names of the ends of the section concerned being displayed in a window in the instrument.
2. There are no lineside signals, merely marker boards, and all instructions to the driver are given by radio by the signaller.
3. Hydro-pneumatic points are provided at the crossing loops. A points indicator is provided to confirm that the points are correctly set and detected for trains entering the loop, while the points can be trailed through without damage by trains leaving the loop in the opposite direction.

4. Safety, which is a major preoccupation of a signaller in a manual signalbox, is largely incorporated in the signalling system equipment itself. In normal circumstances, an IECC signaller cannot move points dangerously, nor give a 'clear' (proceed) signal to a driver when it is unsafe to do so. He does not have to worry about the train acceptance regulations, therefore he can concentrate on his train regulating decisions without the heavy and physically tiring work of the signaller in a manual signalbox.

The stages in the development of signalling technology in the 50 years between Northallerton and the IECC at York have been as follows:

1. The large power signalbox, with routes being set on the entrance-exit principle by push-button or switch.
2. The incorporation of train descriptions on the illuminated diagram panel.
3. Automatic Route Setting.
4. The replacement of the large diagram panel by visual display units.
5. Computer-driven train describer equipment.
6. The replacement of relays by solid-state equipment for interlocking purposes.

On single lines in power signalbox areas it has been quite simple to convert the electric token block system to track circuit block, but in more remote areas electric token block generally reigned supreme until well after World War 2. However, in order to simplify operation, a system known as tokenless block was introduced, in which the use of a token to guarantee that there would be only one

British railway signalling is technically very advanced, and its development might be thought of as a series of steps rather than a gradual smooth process. And it is important to remember that although much of Britain's railway system is signalled by modern methods, there remain hundreds of miles controlled by traditional systems born in the 19th century, together with a number of signalboxes which represent intermediate stages of development, although the latter are disappearing fast.

It goes without saying that if the railways are to be operated safely it is not enough for the signalling system to be modern and foolproof. It is also essential that the message given by the signal arm or light is observed, correctly interpreted and correctly acted upon by the driver. The interface between signal and driver is vital, and the penalty of error is severe. Before the end of the 19th century several railway companies were developing forms of cab signalling to give audible warning to drivers and reinforce the visual message given by the signal. The only system that was developed and installed on a large scale was the Great Western's automatic train control (ATC), although the LMS had a small scale installation of the Hudd system on the London, Tilbury and Southend line. Both systems warned the driver that he was about to pass a distant signal at caution, and both caused the brakes to be applied if the driver failed to acknowledge the warning. After Nationalisation in 1948, the railways started to develop a modification of the Hudd system, which became known as the BR automatic warning system (BR-AWS). Installation started in 1958 and continued over the next 30 years, often in parallel with power signalbox resignalling schemes. Almost all the routes on Britain's railways are now equipped with AWS.

AWS is a fairly simple system, mainly advisory, and although it has been valuable in reducing the number of collisions it has two serious drawbacks:

1. The audible warning does not differentiate between multiple-aspect signals showing two yellows, one yellow, or red, and that situation might mislead the driver. The same warning is also used for permanent and temporary speed restrictions.
2. AWS does not monitor the driver's response to a warning to see that he is braking correctly.

Consideration was therefore given in 1988 to the adoption of a system known as automatic train protection (ATP), and trials were carried out on two routes from London (the Great Western and Chiltern lines). However, the trials were prolonged and not completely satisfactory, and ultimately it was considered that ATP was likely to be too expensive to be cost-effective. It was therefore decided in 1994 not to extend the ATP system to other routes.

However, the abandonment of ATP left the railways no better protected against the consequences of driver error than previously and it was essential that the defects of BR-AWS were remedied as soon as possible in view of the passage of time during the ATP trials. A system was therefore devised known as the Train Protection and Warning System (TPWS). This provides a speed trap on the approach to selected signals which can exhibit a danger aspect, and a trip stop at such signals. The signals selected are those where there are points and crossings in the line ahead, or which have been specially identified as being of a higher risk of being passed at danger. The speed trap has the capability of being effective at speeds up to 75 mph, and is designed to bring to a stand within the overlap any train which it identifies as travelling too fast to stop safely. The trip stop will immediately apply the brakes on any train passing the signal when it is at danger. TPWS is described in more detail in Chapter 21.

The signalling industry, indeed the railway industry as a whole, is now on the verge of a major step forward in the long history of signalling and train control. European Union directives require the European railways, including Britain's railways, to adopt a common system known as the European Train Control System (ETCS). This has a number of features, some of them revolutionary, among which are a standard ATP system, the possible abolition of lineside signals, train position being reported by radio using transponders instead of track circuit or axle counter, and instructions to drivers being given by radio. The West Coast main line is being resignalled and will incorporate some features of ETCS. ETCS is described in more detail in Chapter 22.

Right: **Southern Region postwar signalbox styling at Gloucester Road Junction, March 1954.** *IAL*

Above: **Three-aspect colour light signals at Skipton, with position light signals and route indicators, also signal numberplates and telephones to Leeds power signalbox. The control has now been transferred to York IECC.** *Author*

Colour light signals convey their meaning to the driver in two ways:

1. The colour of the light.
2. The arrangement of the lights when more than one is displayed.

Sometimes the meanings are amplified by illuminated indicators, or modified by the lights flashing on and off.

Colour light running signals are of three types:

1. Signals which can display only two separate aspects. Some signals can display only a red or a green light, whilst others can display only a red or a yellow light, or a yellow or a green light.
2. Signals which can display three aspects — red, yellow or green lights (but only one aspect can be displayed at one and the same time).
3. Signals which can display four aspects — red, one yellow, two yellows, or green lights.

The word 'aspect' means the light, or lights, being displayed. Signals which can display more than two different aspects are known as multiple-aspect signals.

A red light means danger: stop. In normal circumstances, a driver must not pass a signal displaying a red aspect (there are exceptions during failures, and in emergencies, and where otherwise authorised).

One yellow light means caution, and the driver must be prepared to stop at the next signal. In other words, the driver must brake his train so that he can stop at the next signal if it is still showing danger by the time he reaches it.

Two yellow lights, one above the other, tell the driver that he must be prepared to find the next signal displaying one yellow light (or caution if it is a semaphore signal).

A green light means that the line ahead is clear, and that the next signal will be displaying a proceed aspect. A proceed aspect may be either a green light, one yellow light, or two yellow lights, and the term 'proceed aspect' means that the line ahead is clear at least as far as the next signal.

The aspects described so far are known as main aspects, because they control the normal running of trains. The signals are known as running signals. The sequence of signals seen by a driver running up to a red aspect is as shown in the sketch.

Flashing single yellow lights and flashing double yellow lights are used in conjunction with the signalling of some facing junctions and are described in Chapter 7. A facing junction is one which can divert an approaching train on to another route, which may be a geographical divergence or a crossover between two lines, or just another line leading off into, for example, a loop line at a station or a dead-end bay platform.

Colour light signals are used both in colour light areas worked under the track circuit block system, and also as a modern replacement for individual semaphore signals on absolute block lines. In colour light areas all signals

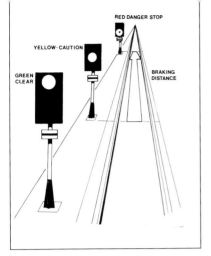

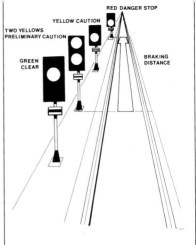

Above: Sequence of signal aspects seen by a driver running up to a red aspect, in a three-aspect area.

Above: Sequence of signal aspects seen by a driver running up to a red aspect, in a four-aspect area.

are of the colour light type. On absolute block lines (see Part 3) it is normally the distant signal which has been converted to a colour light. With certain exceptions a colour light signal on an absolute block line has the same meanings as the night-time indications of a corresponding semaphore signal.

Train movements other than normal direction running movements are known as shunting movements and are controlled by position light signals.

These signals are of two types:

1. Small signals located on the ground, usually about 6ft before facing points. The 'stop' indication is given by one white light and one red light displayed horizontally or by two red lights displayed horizontally. These signals are called Position Light Ground Signals (PLGS).
2. Small signals located below the main aspects of a running signal. They do not have a 'stop' indication because this is given by the main aspect when necessary. These signals are called Position Light Signals. They are unlit, except when required to give a 'proceed' indication.

In each case, the 'proceed' indication is given by the exhibition of two white lights at an angle of 45°, and means:

'The line ahead may be occupied. Proceed cautiously towards the next stop signal (or buffer stops if there is no signal in advance). Be prepared to stop short of any obstruction.'

Where the position light signal is located beneath the main aspects of a running signal, the red main aspect will continue to be displayed when the position light signal shows 'proceed', and the driver may proceed past the signal, even though the main aspect is at danger.

Above: Position light ground signal.
D. C. Hall

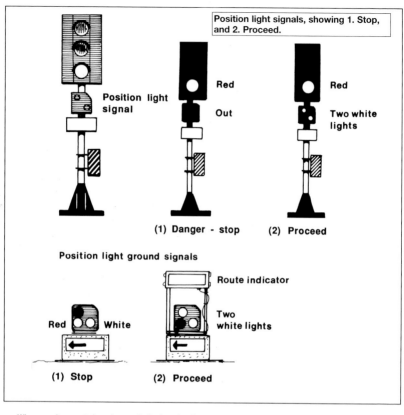

Position light signals, showing 1. Stop, and 2. Proceed.

Position light signal

Red
Out

(1) Danger - stop

Red
Two white lights

(2) Proceed

Position light ground signals

Route indicator

Red   White

Two white lights

(1) Stop

(2) Proceed

When a main aspect shows 'proceed', the line ahead is guaranteed to be clear at least as far as the next main running signal. When a position light signal shows a proceed aspect, there is no such guarantee. Any facing position light ground signals intervening between two main running signals will show 'proceed' when the main aspect in rear shows 'proceed'.

4. Colour Light Signals — Main Aspects. How They are Operated in Colour Light Areas

Colour light signals are divided into three types, depending on the way in which their main aspects are operated:

1. Controlled signals are operated from a signalbox by the signaller and are now identified by a black plate with the signal number shown in white. Earlier plates were white with black characters.

2. Automatic signals are operated by the passage of trains and are identified by a white plate with a horizontal black stripe.

3. Semi-automatic signals are operated by the passage of trains but can also be operated from a signalbox or ground frame. They are identified by a white plate with a horizontal black stripe, and the word SEMI above the stripe.

These plates are fixed to the signalpost.

All three types of signal change to danger when a train passes them and occupies the next track circuit (see Chapter 6). In addition, the signals can be replaced to danger by the signaller in the following ways:

1. Controlled signals. By the signaller pulling out the 'entrance' push-button on his panel (or similar action in the case of other equipment).

2. Automatic signals. By the signaller pulling an emergency replacement button on his panel, adjacent

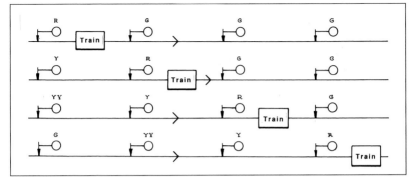

Above: **The effect on the aspect of a four-aspect signal by the presence of a train.**

Right: **Track circuit operating clip in driving cab, ready for instant use.** *Author*

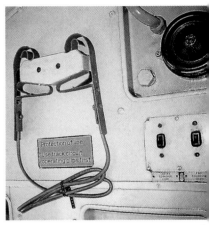

to the signal concerned. In the past it has not been the policy to provide emergency replacement buttons for all automatic signals, but the policy has now been changed and in future all automatic signals will be provided with emergency replacement switches.

3. Semi-automatic signals. By the operation of the ground frame release.

Signals can also be changed to a red aspect (or be held at red) in several ways without the action of a signaller or the normal passage of a train, as follows:

1. By the operation of a switch on the signalpost of those automatic signals which cannot be changed to a red aspect by the signaller, or where there is no confirmation in the signalbox that the signal has actually responded correctly to the signaller's action.
2. By the placing of a track circuit operating clip on the line in advance of the signal. A track circuit operating clip is a device consisting of two metal spring clips joined by a piece of wire. A clip is placed on each rail and this action causes the track circuit to be short-circuited in similar fashion to the wheels of a train passing over it.
3. By anything else which short-circuits the track circuit, eg derailed vehicles from a train on another line.
4. By a broken rail, provided that the rail is not continuously bonded, eg for traction current return purposes. A rail which is completely broken will interrupt a track circuit provided that the track circuit passes through that rail. On some electrified lines

single-rail track circuits are employed; they will not detect a break in the other rail.

5. By a failure of equipment (usually a faulty track circuit). All signalling equipment is designed on the fail-safe principle. Any failures cause signals to change to danger.

Colour light signals are changed from a red aspect to a proceed aspect as follows:

1. Controlled signals. The signaller selects the required route, and sets it by pressing the appropriate push-buttons or other controls. Provided that no part of the required route has already been allocated to another train, and that all the necessary points are free to move, the points will be locked and the route will be set. This fact will be confirmed in power signalboxes by a row of white lights, representing the chosen route, being displayed on the panel. The signal aspect at the start of (or entrance to) the route will change

Left: Track circuit operating clip applied to the track in order to short-circuit the track circuit. *Author*

from red to a proceed aspect, being either one yellow light, two yellow lights, or a green light, depending on how far ahead the line is clear.

2. Automatic signals, and semi-automatic signals acting automatically, will behave as shown in the sketches. In four-aspect signalling, an automatic signal will change to a yellow aspect as soon as the previous train has cleared the safety overlap (normally 200yd) of the next signal in advance (the term 'in advance' means beyond in the direction of travel). When this train clears the safety overlap of the second signal in advance the same automatic signal will change to two yellow lights, known as double yellow, and will in turn change to a green aspect when this train clears the safety overlap of the third signal in advance.

After a controlled signal has been changed to a red aspect by the passage of a train it will remain at red and cannot be changed by the signaller until the route ahead of the signal has been cancelled, either by the signaller himself pulling the entrance button, or by the operation of a device known as train-operated route release (TORR), which automatically releases (or cancels) the route as soon as the train has passed over it. However, some controlled signals can be set by the signaller by push-button to operate automatically. This is a useful device at, for example, a facing junction where the majority of trains travel through the same leg of the junction.

5. Colour Light Signals in Colour Light Areas — The Choice of Type, Location and Spacing

This chapter sets out the principles involved in determining the following issues:

1. Should signals be two-aspect, three-aspect or four-aspect?
2. Should signals be controlled, or automatic?
3. Where should signals be located?

The Choice Between Two-aspect, Three-aspect and Four-aspect

In general the frequency of trains will determine this question. On quiet lines, with trains at half-hourly intervals, two-aspect signals may suffice, with a signal

Left: Co-acting multiple-aspect colour light signals at Manchester Piccadilly Platform 14. The lower signal is provided for the assistance of drivers standing close to the signal. *D. C. Hall*

Above: **'Off' indicator at Liverpool Street conveying a message that the platform starting signal is 'Off'.** *D. C. Hall*

every few miles capable of showing only a red or a green aspect, preceded by another signal acting as a distant signal capable of showing only a yellow or a green aspect. When a two-aspect signal is showing red, the preceding distant signal will display a yellow aspect. When a two-aspect red/green signal shows a green aspect the distant signal will also display a green aspect. The two signals will be braking distance apart, so that a driver travelling at the maximum permitted speed will have time to stop safely at the danger signal after seeing the distant signal at caution.

Braking distance is based on the distance which a train will travel before it stops, after a normal service brake application has been made on a train travelling at the maximum speed allowed on the line at the point at which its brakes are applied. The ruling gradient of the line is taken into account in arriving at the result. Examples follow.

If the frequency of trains requires stop signals to be brought closer together (stop signals are those signals which can display a red aspect), the situation can arise where a stop signal is quite close to the next distant signal beyond. It is unsatisfactory for a driver to be given a green light at one signal followed almost immediately by a yellow light at the next, and it is the practice therefore to combine these two signals in one signal capable of displaying red, yellow and green aspects. These signals are known as multiple-aspect signals, and each one acts not only as a stop signal but also as a distant signal for the next signal in advance. It follows therefore that the signals must at least be at braking distance apart, but not much further than that if unnecessary delays are to be avoided. The latter point is important. A driver will start to

reduce speed when he passes a yellow signal but the next signal, which was at red, may have changed to show a proceed aspect at any time after the driver has passed the yellow signal, and the driver needs to see the next signal as soon as possible so that he can take off the brakes and continue the journey if it has changed to a proceed aspect in the meantime. In practice, three-aspect signals are generally about a mile to a mile and a half apart, depending on the maximum speed allowed on the line concerned.

Where speeds are high or an intensive service is operated requiring trains to follow each other at short intervals (known as close headways), a distance of up to 1½ miles between signals would prove too restrictive and it becomes necessary to introduce additional signals. However, braking distance cannot be reduced, therefore the driver needs to be told, two signals away, that he is approaching a red signal. The first of these two signals seen by the driver acts as a preliminary caution and will display two yellow lights. The second will display one yellow light. As each signal needs to be able to display red, one yellow, two yellows and green we now have four-aspect signalling, with the signals about 1,200yd apart.

There are a number of standards for braking distances (which determine the minimum distance between signals in three-aspect signalling, and between

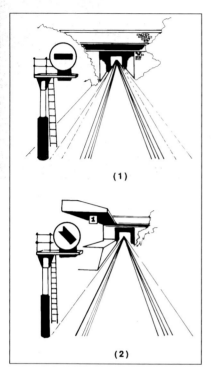

(1)

(2)

Above: **A banner repeating signal, showing 1. Stop signal ahead is 'On', and (2). Distant signal ahead is 'Off'.**

the double-yellow and the red in four-aspect)) based on the type of traffic using the route. The following examples are for routes carrying all types of traffic:

Line speed 125mph	Gradient 1 in 200 rising	2,140yd
	Line level	2,246yd
	Gradient 1 in 200 falling	2,455yd
Line speed 100mph	Gradient 1 in 200 rising	2,056yd
	Line level	2,232yd
	Gradient 1 in 200 falling	2,455yd
Line speed 75mph	Gradient 1 in 200 rising	1,273yd
	Line level	1,375yd
	Gradient 1 in 200 falling	1,511yd

Trains capable of travelling faster than 100mph are equipped with enhanced braking systems.

As we have already seen, automatic signals change from red to a proceed aspect as a train proceeds on its way, but there needs to be some method of maintaining a signal at red at a junction where the signaller may have to stop one train to give prior passage to another. In such circumstances the signal will be capable of being maintained at red by the signaller, and will be known as a controlled signal. Controlled signals are also provided where they protect a non-automatic level crossing, or in certain other circumstances. Some controlled signals are capable of being switched by the signaller to work automatically, but continue to be known as controlled signals. This automatic facility is useful where most train movements over a junction do not require the points to be reset, eg where a lightly used branch line diverges from a busy main line, or at an infrequently used crossover between fast and slow lines.

Signals which protect points, etc worked from a local ground frame are known as semi-automatic. They normally work automatically but can be restored to, or maintained at danger, by the signaller when he wishes to allow a ground frame operator to operate points in the line concerned. The term 'ground frame' (or sometimes 'shunt frame') covers not only an isolated crossover but could also be a former manual signalbox which has been retained to operate points and shunting signals in a marshalling yard or carriage sidings. A ground frame can be regarded as a manual outpost of a signalbox of any type some distance away.

In all other cases, signals work automatically, and are so designated. Automatic signals reduce the signaller's workload and ensure that a proceed aspect is displayed as soon as possible.

The Location of Signals

The location of signals depends upon the following features:

1. Signals are required where trains may need to be stopped, eg at stations and junctions and in yards.
2. Signals should not be located where they might cause trains to be stopped on viaducts or in tunnels, or half-way down one-train-length platforms.
3. Signals should not be located where they might cause level crossings or junctions to be blocked by trains standing across them.
4. Signals are required to divide the line into sections.

The geographical spread of stations, junctions, etc will determine the location of a proportion of signals. The remainder can then be spaced at conventional intervals, bearing in mind the need to provide adequate braking distances.

After a signalling plan has been prepared, it is necessary to consider the practicality of erecting a signal in the planned location. This duty is undertaken by a signal-sighting committee, which will take into account

Right: **Fibre-optic banner repeater for W42 signal at the platform end at London, Vauxhall station. Banner repeaters are provided where the driver's long-distance view of a signal may be impaired by, for example, platform canopies and curved track.**
D. C. Hall

operating and technical requirements and the need to give the driver, as far as possible, a long and clear view of the signal. Where this is not possible, owing to curvature of the line and the presence of obstructions such as bridge abutments, station buildings and platform canopies, etc it may be necessary to provide a banner repeater signal a short distance in rear (ie on the approach side). These signals consist of an illuminated small black semaphore arm in a circular frame. When the main signal is at danger the banner arm will be horizontal; when the main signal is displaying any proceed aspect, the banner arm will be at an angle of 45° from horizontal. The same effect may be achieved by the use of fibre optics.

It will be clear that a certain amount of compromise is inevitable in the location of many signals and it may not be practicable to erect them precisely at braking distance, but they must never be erected at a smaller distance than that. The unavoidable effect of all these factors is that signals may be further from junctions and points than is strictly necessary, leading to inbuilt delay in train working, or that they may have to be spaced out, leading to unnecessarily long braking distances.

6. Detecting the Presence of a Train by Track Circuits or Axle Counters

In colour light areas most running lines are track-circuited. A track circuit is a train detection device which operates by the passage of a weak electric current through one or both of the running rails. Track circuits are of varying lengths, ranging from a minimum of 20yd to a mile or more, and each one is electrically insulated, either physically or electronically, from its neighbour. They are usually of a short length in junction and station areas, and long elsewhere.

In principle, the electric current is fed into the track circuit at one end. At the other end there is a piece of apparatus known as a relay. When there is no train on the track circuit the electric current passes through the relay and causes it to 'open'. When a train enters the section of

line the electric current is diverted through the wheels and axles, away from the relay, which then 'closes'. It has been short-circuited, and the track circuit is said to be 'occupied'.

The track circuit, when occupied, performs a number of vital functions:

1. It holds the signal in rear at danger.
2. It locks facing points in the route.
3. It notifies the presence of a train to the signaller.
4. It can change signals ahead from a danger aspect to a proceed aspect.
5. It enables the train describer in the signalbox to keep in step with train movements.
6. It may be giving warning of a broken rail or an obstruction on the line.

The track circuit has been the very heart of modern signalling. It was originally used as a safeguard against dangerous errors by signallers, who occasionally overlooked the presence of a train standing on the line near their signalbox and cleared their signals, allowing a second train to approach and collide with the first one. A

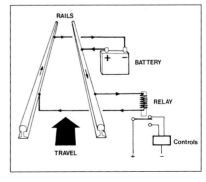

Above: **Method of operation of a track circuit.**

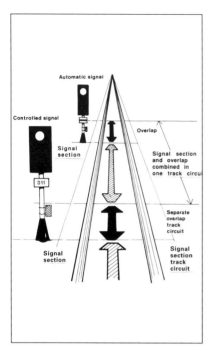

Track circuits play an important role in the concept of the overlap. Originally in semaphore signalling days, a train was allowed to approach a signalbox even though another train was standing on the same line only a few yards ahead of the danger signal, and there were a number of collisions and deaths through drivers mishandling their brakes or not reacting quickly enough to the signal. The overlap at that time was the thickness of the signalpost, but was subsequently standardised at a quarter of a mile. In colour light areas overlaps may vary, but are always less than a quarter of a mile because the sighting of colour light signals spaced at regular intervals is thought to be easier and more reliable than is the case with unevenly spaced distant signals on absolute block lines.

The standard overlap in colour light areas is 200yd. Where speeds are low, shorter overlaps are allowed, eg 50mph — 115yd; 30mph — 77yd.

In the larger through passenger stations where an overall very low speed limit applies to all train movements, very short overlaps may be allowed beyond platform starting signals, so that one train can run into a platform whilst another train is leaving from a different platform but converging on to the same line ahead of the platform starting signal.

Track circuits on open lengths of line are arranged as shown in the diagram left.

Track circuits are used to control the signalling of trains into terminal and bay platform lines where a train or locomotive may need to enter a platform line which is already occupied, and to prevent a train from being admitted into a platform line which is already fully occupied. To achieve this, two track circuits are provided in the platform line, and a second train can only be allowed to enter the platform (under the authority of a position light signal) if the track circuit further from the buffer stops is clear.

If that track circuit is not clear, only a locomotive or two-coach unit may be allowed to enter the platform line. This is controlled by having a short 'measuring' track circuit immediately before the signal. See diagram below.

For a train destined for Platform 1, the arrangements are:

1. If track circuits C, D and E are clear, the signal will display a yellow aspect.
2. If track circuit E is occupied, the signal will display a position light aspect.
3. If track circuits D and E are occupied, the signal will display only a position light aspect if the measuring track circuit B is occupied and track circuits A and C are clear.

Above: **Arrangement of track circuits in rear and in advance of a controlled signal and an automatic signal.**

A controlled signal will show a red aspect as soon as the first pair of wheels occupies the overlap track circuit. An automatic signal will not show a red aspect until the first pair of wheels occupies the track circuit beyond the overlap. This means that a train standing wholly in the overlap beyond an automatic signal will not be protected by that signal, neither will a track circuit operating clip placed on the rails in the overlap put the automatic signal to red.

Axle Counters

Track circuits have reached the limit of their technical potential and have several disadvantages. They are prone to failure in dirty ballast conditions when wet, causing signals to revert to danger. Trains are delayed as a result.

track circuit ensured that a signaller could not clear his signals if a train was standing on the line and 'occupying' the track circuit. For the first time in the development of railway signalling it was no longer necessary for the signaller to actually see the train — the track circuit became his eyes. Coupled with the application of power to the operation of points and signals, the track circuit has allowed signalboxes to control train movements over large areas.

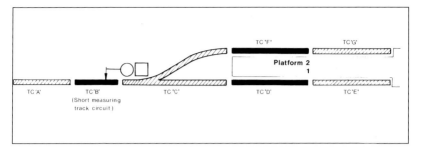

Above: Arrangement of track circuits into bay and terminal platforms, to allow a second train or locomotive to enter safely.

Below: Arrangement of short overlap at a passenger station to facilitate use of the next platform by another train.
A train may be allowed to enter Platform 2 from 'X' at the same time as a train is entering Platform 1 from 'Y' or departing from Platform 1 to 'Y'.

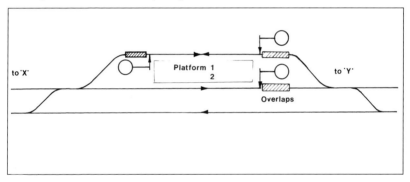

Contaminated rail surfaces, with rust or leaf mulch, may cause track circuits to fail to detect the presence of lightweight trains with few axles. Axle counters are not a new invention, and have been widely used abroad, but until recently they were not considered sufficiently reliable to be used in Britain. However, they have now reached a high standard of reliability and are being increasingly installed in new signalling schemes. They are also replacing track circuits in areas where the latter are causing reliability problems, eg in coastal areas and in tunnels.

Axle counters work on a very simple basis. At the start of a section of line they count the axles of a train passing over them and store the number in a memory. A similar count is made at the end of the section and if the two counts agree, the section is assumed to be clear.

Unfortunately, axle counters are not free from disadvantages. When they are being restored following a failure, very great care must be taken to follow the laid-down procedures precisely. Track circuit operating clips are ineffective (but the availability of train radio can render them unnecessary). They cannot detect obstructions on the line. However, it is likely that train detection and location will increasingly be carried out by radio transmission and balises (transponders) in the future. Track circuits and axle counters might both become redundant, unless they are retained as backup in case of radio system failure.

However, track circuits have provided a valuable means of detecting complete breaks in rails, and permanent way engineers will have to consider how they are to obtain this degree of protection by other means if track circuits are removed. Axle counters cannot detect broken rails and it would be unsatisfactory for the protection afforded by track circuits in the detection of broken rails to be lost. It has already been partially lost on overhead electrified lines, which use only one rail for track circuit purposes, the other rail being used for traction return currents.

These aims are achieved as set out below:

To Inform the Driver Which Way the Junction is Set
There are three methods:

1. A junction indicator, normally located above the junction signal, which indicates the route by displaying a line of white lights, either to the right or left. No route indication is given for the highest speed route, except that where there is no obvious main route a junction indicator will be provided for all routes. Where there are routes of equal speed a junction indicator may be provided for each route. Where the track layout through the switches and crossings straight ahead appears to the driver to be a legitimate route, but which actually leads to an unsignalled route (eg a route used only by trains running in the opposite direction), a junction indicator will be provided for all signalled routes.
2. A multi-lamp alpha-numeric route indicator, located on the same post as the junction signal. This may be used only where train speeds do not exceed 80mph.
3. By offsetting the signal for the diverging route to one side of the running signal.

Approach Control and Release of the Junction Signal
Except where the difference in maximum permitted speed between the main route and the turnout at the points to the diverging route is 10mph or lower, the junction signal is normally held at red (or yellow) for a period when the points are set for the diverging route, to ensure that the driver receives caution aspects at the preceding signals and reduces the speed of the train. However, the junction signal may clear to yellow as soon as the route is set at those layouts where a train braking to stop at the next signal beyond the junction would not pass through the junction at more than its designed speed plus 10mph.

In the majority of cases, junction signals are approach-released from red, and this may take effect at any time after the approaching train has passed the previous signal, subject to the following provisos:

1. The proceed aspect at the junction signal must not become visible to the driver before the route indicator (for example, where the junction signal is beyond an overbridge which restricts the view of the junction indicator). In such cases, the junction signal must be held at red until the route indicator is visible. This is to avoid misleading the driver into thinking he is being signalled along the straight route and consequently travelling too fast when he finally sees the junction indicator.
2. Wherever possible, approach release should take effect before the driver can see the signal.

Above: **Three-aspect colour light signal with direction indicator at Wigan Wallgate.** *J. H. Edser*

7. Junction Signalling in Colour Light Areas

(The term junction as used here refers to any set of facing points in the normal direction of running. It covers not only a geographical junction, where the line splits off into two different directions, but also a track layout where the facing points give access to a parallel running line, or to a diverging platform line at a station.)

The signals which drivers see when approaching facing junctions have additional roles to play, besides telling the drivers whether the line ahead is clear or not. These additional roles are:

1. To inform the driver which way the junction is set.
2. To ensure that he reduces speed as necessary when the junction is set for a diverging route where the degree of curvature in the points and beyond demands the imposition of a speed limit. This is known as approach control.
3. To ensure that the points cannot move when the junction signal is displaying a proceed aspect.

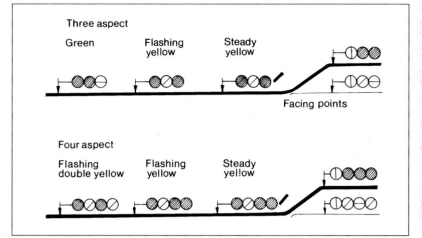

Three aspect

Green   Flashing   Steady
          yellow   yellow

Facing points

Four aspect

Flashing   Flashing   Steady
double yellow   yellow   yellow

Where the diverging junction has been specially laid to allow higher speeds, and where approach release from red would not allow the planned level of speed through the diverging junction to be achieved, the junction signal may display an unrestricted yellow aspect to the highest speed diverging route, and the previous signal a flashing yellow aspect. In four-aspect territory, the signal before that will display two flashing yellows. The junction signal itself is released in the same manner as described for approach release from red. Where there are successive junctions, and both are suitable for flashing yellow signalling, it may only be applied to one of the junctions.

So far as the driver is concerned, he has to remember that a single flashing yellow light not only means that the junction ahead has been set for the highest speed diverging route, but may also mean preliminary caution because the next signal but one is at danger. However, if the line ahead is clear, the driver will see the following sequence of signals in four-aspect territory:

- Two flashing yellow lights
- One flashing yellow light
- Steady yellow light with junction indicator at the junction signal, changing to green (depending on sighting conditions, the junction signal may already be at green when it comes within the driver's sight).

Directing Distant Signals (Commonly known as Splitting Distants)
At certain junctions where other forms of junction signalling are not appropriate, eg at very high speed junctions or where there are successive high speed junctions, splitting distants may be provided at the signal in rear of the junction signal, and where necessary at the

Above: **Sequence of aspects seen by the driver at a junction provided with flashing yellow signalling.**

second signal in rear of the junction signal. These take the form of additional green and yellow heads offset from main signal heads. The junction signal will not be subject to approach release.

Temporary Speed Restriction on Diverging Route
Where there is a temporary speed restriction on a diverging route it is essential that drivers know which way the junction points are set so that they can reduce speed as necessary for the temporary speed restriction. Therefore, where the junction is normally signalled to allow for higher speeds, a temporary approach release from red arrangement must be applied to hold the junction signal at red until the route indication is readable by the driver.

Approach Locking of Points
The purpose of approach locking is to prevent a route ahead of a signal from being changed once the driver has seen a proceed aspect at the junction signal (or a green aspect two signals away or a double-yellow aspect at the previous signal). However, provision is made for the locking to be released provided that, if the junction signal is replaced to danger, sufficient time has elapsed either for the train to have come to a stand at the junction signal, or to have run past it on to track circuits which lock the points.

Approach locking becomes operative immediately a proceed aspect has been displayed at the junction signal.

Left: Clamp-lock-operated points. *D. C. Hall*

Approach locking is released in the following ways:

1. When the train passes the signal.
2. By the operation of a time release, which is generally between one and four minutes depending on the distance between signals, the type of traffic on the line concerned (passenger only, or mixed traffic), and the nature of the location (eg a major station or critical junction).

There are some other items regarding points, which might be mentioned:

1. A junction signal must not be more than half a mile from the facing points (or the first of a series).
2. Flank protection may be provided at junctions to protect a train from another one approaching the junction, which may have run past a signal at danger (see diagram on page 28). Before signal 2 can be cleared, points Y must be set towards C to protect a train proceeding from C to B against another train requiring to proceed from B to A which may wrongly have passed signal 1 at danger. In more complex layouts, it is similarly preferable for an overrunning train to be diverted onto a line used predominantly by trains in the same direction.
3. If a driver finds that a junction signal has been cleared for the wrong route, or that he receives flashing yellow aspects when he is expecting to proceed along the highest speed route, or that he receives clear signals at signals in rear of a junction at which he is expecting to be diverted, he must stop at the junction signal if possible (and safe) and speak to the signaller.

Left: Theatre-type (also known as multi-lamp) route indicators at the south end of Derby station. *IAL*

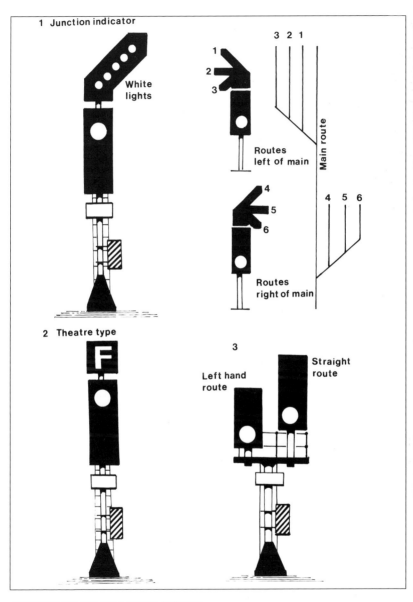

1 Junction indicator

White lights

1
2
3

Routes left of main

3 2 1

Main route

4
5
6

Routes right of main

4 5 6

2 Theatre type

F

3

Left hand route

Straight route

Above: The different types of route indicator:
1. White lights;
2. Multi-lamp;
3. Offset signal.

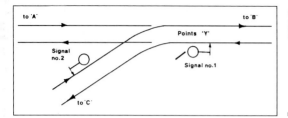

Left: An example of flank protection at a double junction.

to 'A'

to 'B'

Points 'Y'

Signal no.2

Signal no.1

to 'C'

8. Inside a Modern Power Signalbox

The large power signalboxes which control main lines in Britain were mostly brought into use in the 1960s and 1970s. Generally speaking, the technical equipment is housed on the ground floor or lower floors, whilst the operating room is located on the upper floor.

The most distinctive feature of the operating room is the control panel, which usually occupies the full length of one side, or may even be horseshoe-shaped. The panel

Above: Communication from platform staff to signalman, guard and driver at Liverpool Street: 'TRS' ('Train ready to start') sends a message to the signalman; 'Barrier Bell' sends a message to close the ticket barrier; 'CD' signals 'Close doors' (a message from the platform staff to the guard, or driver of a driver-only-operated train; 'RA' signals 'Right away', a message to the driver. The 'RA' will not illuminate at the signal until the signal itself is cleared.
D. C. Hall

displays a geographical representation of all the lines controlled from the signalbox and contains all the operating switches and buttons for use by the signallers, of whom there may be any number from two to a dozen or more. Behind the signallers are a number of desks for train regulators, supervisors, announcers and assistants, etc.

The signaller's role is to set the routes for trains, and clear the signals, in accordance with the timetable, and when trains run late it is his job to minimise the effect of such late running. He therefore needs to know about trains approaching his area of control so that he can make the most appropriate regulating decisions, and he can see where all trains are by looking at the control panel.

In order to set a route and clear the signals for a train the signaller presses the entrance button alongside the first controlled signal on his control panel. The button will then show a white flashing light. He then presses the exit button at the next controlled signal along the route to be taken by the approaching train (one button normally serves as both an entrance and an exit button). If the route is available (ie has not been 'promised' to another train), all the points will be switched to their appropriate position, and locked, for the safety of the train, and if all the track circuits concerned are clear the first controlled signal will switch to a proceed aspect. The signal indication on the control panel will show a green light irrespective of whether the lineside signal itself is showing green, one yellow or two yellows. A row of white lights will be displayed on the control panel along the route concerned to confirm to the signaller that it has been successfully set. The signaller will then repeat the procedure further along the route to be taken by the train until the whole of the route within the signaller's area of control has been set.

When the train enters the route concerned and occupies the first track circuit its presence will be indicated to the signaller by a number of red lights on the line on his control panel, and as the train moves along and occupies and subsequently clears further track circuits the row of red lights on the control panel will step along accordingly, so that the signaller can always tell which track circuit is being occupied by the train. He cannot normally tell exactly where the train is if only one track circuit is showing occupied, but if two are showing

Right: Close-up view of part of the panel at Feltham power signalbox. *IAL*

Left: Interior of Wolverhampton power signalbox. *IAL*

Below: Derby power signalbox, showing a signalman operating the panel. At the top of the panel are the individual switches for operating points when required. *IAL*

occupied it is a fair deduction that the train is straddling the boundary between them.

As the train proceeds on its way the signals will change to danger behind it, but the row of white route lights will remain on the control panel until either the signaller cancels the route by pulling out the entrance button, or they are extinguished by the automatic operation of train-operated route release equipment, which is provided where it is reasonable to do so.

To enable the signaller to carry out his regulating duties he needs to know the identity of trains. All trains in the timetable have a unique four-character identity number and each train displays its number on the control panel in windows or berths along the route concerned. As the train proceeds and occupies track circuits in sequence, the train description displayed on the control panel steps forward from berth to berth accordingly (a berth is normally the track circuit in rear of a signal). There is one exception to this in older power signalboxes: if the train passes a signal at danger the track circuit indications on the control panel will step forward normally, but the train description will remain in the berth on the approach side of the signal concerned, ie the train description will not pass a signal at danger. This provides important evidence in cases where a signal is wrongly passed at danger and the aspect displayed by the signal is disputed by the driver.

In most signalboxes the control panel is arranged almost vertically and combines both the controls and the indications. The signaller walks to and fro to reach the various controls on that section of the panel under his jurisdiction. In some of the larger and busier signalboxes, eg London Bridge and Victoria, the controls are removed from the panel and provided on a separate console at which the signaller sits. This is more expensive but enables the signaller to have a wider overview of the panel and may lead to the improved regulation of trains in dense and complex traffic conditions.

The control panels contain other equipment besides the geographical display, such as:

1. Individual point switches, for movement of the points in special circumstances.
2. Indicators, showing which way the points are lying. The two positions are known as normal and reverse. There is a third indication, known as 'out of correspondence', which is illuminated when the points have failed to move across correctly from one position to the other, or when they have been damaged in an accident. Signals will not clear if points are showing 'out of correspondence'.
3. Telephones, giving communication at each signal with drivers and anyone else who may need to speak to the signaller, eg trackmen and signal technicians. When the telephone is used, the number of the signal at which the telephone is located is displayed on the panel to assist the signaller in identifying the origin of the call. The rules also require the caller to identify himself and say where he is standing. Communication can often only be established from the signal to the signalbox; the signaller may not be able to ring the telephone instrument at the signal. He should normally not need to do so and it reduces the cost of the equipment.

4. Telephones, giving communication to stations, offices, etc, through the normal railway telephone network.
5. Radio equipment at some signalboxes, giving communication with drivers.
6. Level crossing indications and controls.
7. Hot axlebox warning equipment.
8. 'Train ready to start' (TRS) indications. At larger stations, where trains may be detained for reasons not apparent to the signaller, it may be an advantage for the setting of the route to be delayed until the train is ready to depart, thus allowing the route to be used by other trains. The signaller is then informed that the train is ready to depart, by the operation of a plunger on the platform by the supervisor, which causes a yellow light to flash on the control panel at the end of the platform concerned.
9. Releases to ground frames, shunt frames, level crossing boxes, etc.
10. Emergency replacement buttons and indications, for automatic and semi-automatic signals.
11. Automatic working of controlled signals. The signaller can convert a controlled signal to automatic operation by pressing an 'A' button sited next to the signal on his panel, after the route has been set. The 'A' button will then show a white light. Automatic operation can be cancelled at any time merely by pulling out the 'A' button, but such action will not cancel the route.

In the most recent signalboxes(known as Integrated Electronic Control Centres [IECCs]), eg York and Southall, the signaller's control panel has been replaced by visual display units (VDUs) and tracker-ball/keyboard operation. The whole of the track layout, together with all the indications, is not permanently displayed, but the signaller calls up (ie displays) on his screens the particular areas or indications that he requires. The screens are capable of displaying either an overview covering a relatively large area but omitting some detail, or a smaller area including such detail. The principles of operation remain the same — in order to set a route, the signaller, by using the tracker-ball, moves the cursor on his VDU screen to the signal at the entrance to the route he wishes to set, then enters his command. He then moves the cursor to the exit signal of the route and activates the setting of the route. Alternatively the signaller can set the route by the use of the keyboard, entering the numbers of the entrance and exit signals.

VDU equipment is cheaper, and requires far less space, than conventional control panels; consequently the operating room can be smaller. Coupled with the technical change from relay interlocking to solid-state interlocking, the whole signalbox structure can be smaller.

A predictable and repetitive train service lends itself readily to the use of computer-controlled automatic route-setting equipment. Routes are set by the computer as programmed, including decisions on priorities at junctions, and alterations in the case of late running.

Event recorders are installed in modern signalboxes which record such things as signal aspect changes, the lie of points, etc. This information is especially useful to people investigating mishaps.

9. Colour Light Signalling — Miscellaneous

Signalling a Passenger Train into an Occupied Platform (Permissive Working)

When the signaller wishes to set up a route for a passenger train from a controlled signal onto an occupied Permissive Platform Line he will press the normal entrance and exit buttons, but the main signal aspect will remain at red, owing to the occupation of a track circuit in the route ahead. In such circumstances, authority for the driver to proceed will be given by the exhibition of two white lights inclined at 45° in the associated position light signal. These are the only circumstances in which the driver of a passenger train in service may proceed on the authority of a position light signal. In the case of a through platform line at a station where the train is not booked to call, the signaller must advise the driver of the circumstances before clearing the signal.

Permissive working of this nature should be avoided if possible in new works by, for example, the provision of mid-platform signals.

Lamp Failures in Colour Light Running Signals (Lamp Proving)

All lamps have both a main filament and an auxiliary filament. Any failure of a main filament causes an indication of the fact to be given in the signalbox. If a lamp, which should be illuminated, fails completely, the next main running signal on the approach side will be maintained at red, in order to ensure safety.

Numbering of Colour Light Signals

Each signalpost carries a plate bearing the signal identity, comprising one or two prefix letters usually representing the controlling signalbox, followed by a number unique to that prefix. Odd numbers are used for the down direction, with the numbers ascending in the direction of the traffic flow. Even numbers are used for the up direction, descending in the direction of the traffic flow. Automatic signals are identified as such to the driver by a horizontal black band on the identity plate. Semi-automatic signals carry the word SEMI on the plate, above the horizontal band.

(Older installations may vary from the above.)

Remote Control Standby Arrangements

Standby arrangements, known as override facilities, are provided at the older power signalboxes to deal with any failure of the cable between the signalbox and remote interlockings. These standby arrangements enable train movements to continue, but line capacity is reduced. In newer installations the control link (known as TDM) is duplicated to avoid the provision of expensive override facilities and to reduce the disruption of train services.

Signals from Sidings on to Running Lines

A main signal (rather than a position light ground signal) is provided at the exit from sidings where there are regular rightaway movements and the next signal ahead is not visible from the siding exit (or is a long distance ahead).

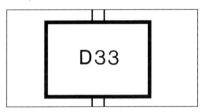

Above: **The numberplate of a controlled signal.**

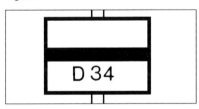

Above: **The numberplate of an automatic signal.**

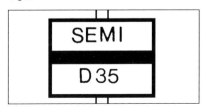

Above: **The numberplate of a semi-automatic signal.**

Right: A hybrid signalbox at Stafford No 4 with an illuminated diagram, colour light signals and power-operated points worked from a mechanical frame. *IAL*

Below: New type of signal at Reading using light-emitting diodes (LEDs) instead of light-bulbs. LED signals will be used increasingly all over the network.

Colour Light Signals Not in Use
When main or position light aspects are not in use they are covered over. A large X may also be exhibited over the cover of main aspects.

Delayed Yellow Operation
Where it is operationally desirable to allow a passenger train to approach a signal without the full overlap being available, the next signal in rear is held at red until the train is close to it, after which it will clear to yellow. This is to ensure that the speed of the train is suitably reduced, and is a colour light version of the absolute block 'section clear but station or junction blocked' warning arrangement.

10. Colour Light Areas — Emergencies

Complete Failure of Signalling Apparatus
In the event of a complete failure of signalling apparatus affecting two or more consecutive stop signals along a route, a substitute system of Temporary Block Working is

introduced. Handsignallers are appointed and there must be communication between them and the signaller. Handsignallers are appointed at signals at strategic locations and emergency block working is introduced between them, under the instructions of the signaller. The handsignaller completes a temporary block working ticket and gives it to the driver. The ticket may authorise the driver to pass two or more consecutive signals.

There are detailed instructions in the *Rule Book (Section D)* and the *Train Signalling Regulations Book (TCB Regulation 11.7)*.

Track Circuit Irregularities
When track circuits fail to operate correctly they are designed to fail safe, ie they switch protecting signals to danger and lock points etc. Any failure which did not initiate such safeguards would be very serious; failures of that type, fortunately rare, are known as wrong-side failures.

A signaller becomes aware of such an irregularity, commonly but incorrectly called a track circuit failure, when the red track circuit lights are illuminated on his

Right: The transition stage at Northallerton. Northallerton junction signal N54, complete with route-indicator, position-light signal, signal number plate, white diamond plate (indicating the provision of a track circuit) and a telephone to the signaller. It was in turn replaced by York IECC signal No Y467, which was brought into use on 14 April 1990. *Ian S. Carr*

panel when there is no train on that section of the line, or when the red lights fail to go out after a train has passed and the following track circuit has cleared. The most likely cause is a failure of equipment, but the signaller must not assume that such is the cause. On the contrary, he must assume that the line may be obstructed, and he must find out whether it is or not. In the meantime, trains will be at a standstill because the protecting signal will be at red.

Unless the signaller can establish that the line is clear (eg by telephoning a station supervisor if the track circuit concerned is near the station), he must arrange for the line to be examined. It is usually most convenient for this to be done by using a train, and if one will pass over an adjacent line before one passes over the affected line the driver must be informed of the circumstances, instructed to proceed at caution, prepared to stop short of any obstruction, and to report his findings. He need not be accompanied specially.

The first train over the affected line must be stopped. The driver must then be instructed to pass the signal held at danger, proceed at caution and report the state of the line to the signaller. If the affected track circuit is wholly or partly in a tunnel, speed must not exceed 10mph.

Any class of train may be used irrespective of the weather conditions.

If it is established that there is no obstruction causing the track circuit to show occupied, it must be considered as having failed, and following trains may be allowed to proceed, each driver being authorised to pass the

protecting signal at danger. However, whilst the failure exists, the signaller has no way of knowing whether the piece of line concerned is clear or not, therefore he must take one of two possible precautions:

1. Appoint someone suitable to stand at the track circuit to report whether it is clear after each train has passed.
2. Carefully watch, on his panel, the passage of each train and see that it occupies and clears the track circuit ahead of the signal beyond the failed track circuit. Drivers must be instructed to proceed cautiously, because the signaller cannot be 100% sure that the line is clear.

Examination of Line

If there is reason to believe, owing to some emergency or other, that the line may be blocked or unsafe to use, a train may be allowed to enter the section on any line in the right direction to examine the line. The term 'examination of line' is not confined solely to the track itself but includes anything out of the ordinary that may cause danger to a train. It also includes all lines in the section concerned, not just the line that the train is running on. The precise Rule Book wording 'Examine the line to see if it is clear' really means 'look out for any source of danger on any line'. Certain provisos have to be observed:

1. The signaller must be satisfied that the last train signalled has passed clear of the overlap of the signal

beyond the portion of line concerned.

2. The driver need not be accompanied, except during darkness, fog or falling snow or in a tunnel, when the guard or other competent person must, if immediately available, accompany the driver.

3. If definite information is received that someone has fallen from a train, the driver must be accompanied in conditions of poor visibility as defined in (2) above.

4. The train's headlight must be lit in conditions of poor visibility.

The purpose of having the driver accompanied is to provide an extra pair of eyes. 'Competent' means having sufficient railway experience to be able to recognise a potential hazard, but see the Rule Book Glossary: 'A person who has been passed as being qualified and having the required knowledge and skills to carry out a particular Rule, Regulation, Instruction or Procedure'.

The driver of the examining train must be told about what is going on, and that he must proceed at caution ready to stop at any moment if he sees an obstruction or any other source of danger ahead. He must then report at the next signal ahead. Care is needed if there are catch points, and if the affected portion of line is in a tunnel the driver must not exceed 10mph when passing through it.

After the examining train has entered the affected section of line, no other train may enter the same section on the same or an adjacent line until the signaller has received a report stating which lines are safe for trains to run on.

Report of a Suspected Track Defect

From time to time, drivers feel a bump or jolt which is more severe than the usual bumps which are part and parcel of most journeys. They must then stop at the first available signal and report the facts to the signaller so that following trains can be stopped in case a dangerous defect has developed in the track or it is obstructed in some way. It is quite possible that by the time the signaller has received the report, a following train may also have passed over the bump, but it will probably be running under caution signals and slowing down.

The signaller must then arrange for the line to be examined as described in the previous section 'Examination of Line'. If no reason for the bump can be found, normal working may be resumed on other lines, but on the affected line drivers must be stopped and told about what has happened and instructed to proceed cautiously. This procedure must be continued for each following train until the affected line has been examined and confirmed to be safe by a person in charge of work on railway infrastructure. It is important that drivers reporting a bump should be as precise as possible regarding its location and at all costs avoid giving a misleading location. It is equally important that the Civil

Engineering contractor's staff are sure that any defect they find is the one reported by the driver.

Suspected Damage to Track or Structures

A train must not pass over a portion of line affected by subsidence or by suspected damage to a structure above or beneath the railway unless the signaller has been assured that it is safe for the train to do so, travelling at reduced speed if necessary.

If a railway bridge over a road has been hit by a road vehicle (an occurrence known as bridge bashing), trains must be stopped until the bridge has been examined. If a Bridge Examining Engineer is not immediately available, the bridge may be examined by a Bridge Strike Nominee. If the damage is only superficial, the Bridge Strike Nominee may allow trains to pass over the bridge at 5mph in the case of a rail-over-road bridge, or up to 20mph where the bridge is over the railway, pending an examination by a Bridge Examining Engineer. The *Rule Book Section V* gives very detailed guidance on these issues.

Broken Rails in Continuously Welded Track

A broken rail may be detected in a number of ways:

1. If there is a gap between the two broken ends, any track circuit current flowing through the rail will be interrupted, causing the track circuit indication on the signalbox panel to show occupied, and switching the signal in rear (ie on the approach side) to danger.

2. It may be noticed by the track patrolman on his regular routine inspection or by some other member of staff.

3. A driver passing over the spot may feel an unusual bump, which he will stop and report, leading to an examination of the track.

The question then arises as to whether trains may be allowed to pass over the break. If a person competent in track examination is not immediately available, someone who has been certified as competent in the instructions in Section V of the Rule Book may authorise trains to proceed over a broken or distorted rail at 5mph provided that certain conditions are met, including the following:

• the rail is in plain line
• the rail is not in a tunnel
• the adjacent sleepers and fastenings are in good condition
• the detailed conditions listed in the Rule Book concerning the nature of the break or damage are applied.

The rail must be carefully examined before each train passes over it, to ensure that it is safe to do so. Whilst a train is passing over the break, no train may be allowed to pass over an adjoining line (a safety precaution in case the train passing over the break becomes derailed).

PART 3

11. The Absolute Block System of Signalling

Left: A typical ex-Midland Railway mechanical signalbox at Oakham.
D. C. Hall

In order to send train-signalling messages from one signalbox to the next one, a bell system is used with the messages being described by the number and pattern of beats on the bell. Instruments, known as block indicators, are provided in each signalbox for each section and each direction. In the controlling signalbox the standard block indicator can be moved to one of three positions — normal (line blocked), line clear, and train on line. In the rear signalbox there is a slave block instrument which copies the indication of the block instrument in the controlling signalbox.

When there is no train in the area the line is considered blocked, which might be considered a misnomer. What it means is that the line is not at that moment being used by a train, therefore it is temporarily out of use and must not be considered to be clear until the signaller says that it is. It is also a means of compelling the signaller at the box in rear to ask for permission to send a train through the section. At some signalboxes there are older block instruments of different types, which date back to the old pre-1923 companies.

If we consider our three signalboxes A, B and C again, the method of passing a train along the line is as follows:

When the signaller at box A wishes to arrange for a train to proceed from A to B he will call the attention of the signaller at box B by sending one beat on the bell (known as the block bell). B will respond with one beat. A will then send the appropriate bell signal for the type of train (eg four beats for an express passenger train). If B is satisfied that there is no train in the section A-B and that the line is clear to the clearing point, also that the block indicator for that section is at the normal position (Line blocked), he may accept the train by repeating the four beats bell signal and moving his block indicator to 'Line clear'. The slave indicator in box A will also move to 'Line clear' as a reminder to the signaller there, and he may then clear his signals for the train. In most signalboxes there is an electrical lock on the most advanced signal which prevents the signal from being cleared until the block indicator shows 'Line clear'. Furthermore, as an additional precaution, the signal can only be cleared once for each 'Line clear'.

This is the traditional way of signalling trains, which was developed during the 19th century and refined during the first half of the 20th, but is now largely superseded on main lines by the track circuit block system. However, there are still several hundreds of the familiar signalboxes on secondary lines.

The absolute block system might be summed up in the principle, set out in the Regulations for many, many years, 'To ensure that not more than one train shall be in a block section on the same line at the same time'.

So what is a block section? It is that piece of line between the last signal passed by a train at one signalbox and the first stop signal at the next signalbox.

The last signal passed by a train at a signalbox controls the entrance to a block section and is known as a Section Signal (or sometimes as the most advanced signal). The first stop signal at a signalbox is known as the Home Signal. At some signalboxes there may be more than one Home Signal, known variously as Outer and Inner Home Signals, or Home Nos 1 and 2 Signals. In such cases the first one to be encountered by a train is known as the Outermost Home Signal (or alternatively the Outermost Stop Signal).

The section of line between the outermost stop signal and the most advanced signal worked from the same signalbox is known as 'station limits', irrespective of the existence of a station there or not.

In railway parlance, the terms advanced and rear may be confusing and are best illustrated in the diagram.

So far as signalbox B is concerned, for a train travelling from A to C the rear section is A-B; the advance section is B-C.

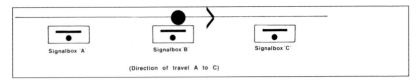

Signalbox 'A' Signalbox 'B' Signalbox 'C'

(Direction of travel A to C)

Above: **An illustration of the meaning of the terms 'rear section' and 'advance section' (see text).**

When the train passes A, the signaller there must send the 'Train entering section' signal to B, who must repeat it back and move his block indicator to 'Train on line'. B must then seek acceptance of the train from the signaller at C and clear his own signals.

When the train passes B, the signaller will send the 'Train entering section' signal to C, and when the train has passed the 'clearing point' at B (normally a quarter of a mile past the outermost stop signal at B), complete with tail lamp, the signaller at B will call the attention of A (one beat) and, having obtained it (one beat repeated back), will send the 'Train out of section' signal (two beats, pause, one beat) and move the block indicator to the normal position (line blocked). A can now offer (ie seek acceptance of) another train to B.

To avoid the danger that might arise if a signaller were mistakenly to give the 'Train out of section' signal whilst the train is still in the rear section, special equipment is provided at some signalboxes which locks the block indicator at 'Train on line' until the train is proved to have passed through the section by the occupation of a track circuit, or the actuation of a treadle, at the home signal. A release mechanism is provided in case of equipment failure, or if a train which has been signalled forward is cancelled, and there are three different release systems in use:

1. The 'Welwyn' Control system. Before the block indicator can be released, a small wheel has to be rotated about a hundred times, which gives the signaller time for second thoughts and allows a train still in the rear section more time to reach the home signal and safety. It has proved a very effective system since it was first introduced following an accident at Welwyn Garden City in 1935, and is now the standard system.
2. Sykes 'Lock and Block'. Introduced in the last century and at one time in widespread use, especially on the lines of the former Southern Railway, but now replaced in most cases by modern power signalling. The release takes the form of a key, but its misuse has caused a number of accidents.
3. Midland Railway Rotary Block. The block instrument

can only be moved in rotation from the normal position, through 'Line clear', to 'Train on line', then back to normal. To cancel a 'Line clear', both signallers have to agree and press a cancelling button simultaneously. To release the block indicator from 'Train on line' the signaller has to press a button to which access can be gained only by breaking a glass cover. The signaller must then send a report to his supervisor and call for the Signalling Maintenance staff to replace the glass cover.

Every train carries a tail lamp behind the rear vehicle to prove to the signaller that the train is complete, and that no part of it has been accidentally left in the rear section. Signallers must carefully observe the tail lamp before sending the 'Train out of section' signal.

Where sections are short, the signaller may be authorised to send the 'Is line clear' signal to the box in advance as soon as he has accepted the train from the box in rear. This avoids drivers seeing the signals before they have been cleared, which would cause delay.

Where a signaller needs to know about the approach of a train before he receives the 'Train entering section' signal, eg to give him time to close level crossing gates or barriers across the road, the signaller in rear may be authorised to send the 'Train approaching' signal (1-2-1) when the train passes a pre-determined point (usually the previous signalbox).

The bell codes used to signal trains in the Absolute Block System are as follows:

Class of train	No of beats
Call attention	1
Is line clear for:	
Class 1 Train	4
Class 9 Passenger 373/1 or 373/2 train	1-4
Class 2 Train	3-1
Class 3 Train	1-3-1
Class 4 Train	3-1-1
Class 5 Train	2-2-1
Class 6 Train	5
Class 7 Train	4-1
Class 8 Train	3-2
Class 9 Empty Coaching Stock 373/1 or or 373/2 train	1-4-1
Class 0 Locomotive(s)	2-3
Train Required to Stop in Section	2-2-3

Details of the classes are as follows:

Classification Description

1 Express passenger train
  Nominated postal or parcels train
  Breakdown or overhead line equipment train going to clear the line or returning therefrom (1Z99)
  Traction unit going to assist a disabled train (1Z99)
  Snowplough going to clear the line (1Z99)
  Class 9 373/1 or 373/2 train

2 Ordinary passenger train
  Breakdown or overhead line equipment train not going to clear the line (2Z99)
  Officer's Special train (2Z01)

3 Freight train capable of running at more than 75mph, or a parcels train or an empty coaching stock train where specially authorised.

4 Freight train permitted to run at more than 60mph

5 Empty coaching stock train

6 Freight train permitted to run at 50, 55 or 60mph

7 Freight train permitted to run at 40 or 45mph

8 Freight train permitted or timed to run at 35mph or less

0 Light locomotive(s)

Other bell signals are:	*No of beats*
Train entering section	2
Train approaching	1-2-1
Cancelling	3-5
Train incorrectly described	5-3
Restricted acceptance	3-5-5
Line now clear in accordance with Reg 3, clause 3.4, for the train to approach	3-3-5
Train out of section ⎤ Obstruction removed ⎦	2-1
Locomotive assisting in rear of train	2-2
Obstruction danger	6
Train an unusually long time in section	6-2
Stop and examine train	7
Train passed without tail lamp ⎰ 9 to box in advance ⎱ 4-5 to box in rear	
Train or vehicles running away in wrong direction	2-5-5
Train or vehicles running away in right direction	4-5-5

There are a number of other bell signals which we need not concern ourselves with.

The Call Attention signal (1 beat) must be sent and acknowledged before any other bell signal is sent, except for the following:

	No of beats
Train entering section	2
Train approaching	1-2-1
Restricted acceptance	3-5-5
Locomotive assisting in rear of train	2-2
Obstruction danger	6
Police assistance urgently required	1-1-6
Answer telephone	1-1
Distant signal defective	8-2
Home signal defective	2-8

Generally speaking, bell signals are acknowledged by repetition and must not be considered as correctly understood until correctly repeated. If the 'Is line clear' signal is not acknowledged (ie if the request for acceptance is refused) it must be sent again at short intervals. In railway parlance, trains are offered and either accepted or refused.

The bell signal 'Answer telephone' is only to be used for the block telephone, which is a special circuit connecting only the two signalboxes.

Train Regulation

Trains must generally take precedence according to classification.

12. Semaphore Signals — What They Mean

Semaphore signals consist of the following:

• Distant signals
• Stop signals
• Subsidiary signals
• Shunting signals

Distant and Stop Signals

Distant and stop signals are used to control normal train movements. A distant signal takes the form of a rectangular yellow arm with a fish-tail end and a black chevron. A stop signal has a red rectangular arm and a white vertical stripe. The backs of the arms are white, with a black chevron or bar, to indicate that they are not applicable when approached from the back.

The indications to drivers are as follows:

Distant Signals

When the arm is horizontal the driver must get ready to stop at the next stop signal. When the arm is pivoted upwards or downwards through approximately 45° it means that all stop signals for the line concerned which are worked from the same signalbox are clear. At night the caution indication is given by a yellow light. The clear indication is given by a green light.

Stop Signals

When the arm is horizontal (red light at night) it means 'stop'. When the arm is pivoted up or down through approximately 45° (green light at night) it means 'proceed'.

A subsidiary signal is placed below the main arm of a stop signal and takes the form of a small red arm (or a white arm with horizontal red stripes). Subsidiary signals are of two types, called calling-on signals and shunt-ahead signals. They are distinguished by a letter 'C' or 'S'.

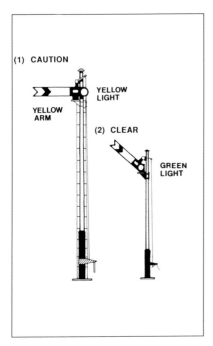

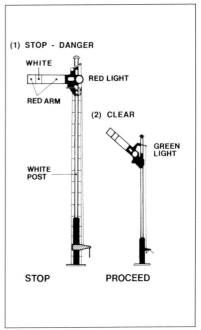

Above: A distant signal, showing 1. Caution, and 2. Clear.

Above: A stop signal, showing 1. Stop — danger, and 2. Clear.

They have no meaning when the arm is horizontal (although they may show a red or white light), but when the arm is pivoted up or down by approximately 45° they mean:

Calling-on Signals:
Proceed cautiously towards the next stop signal (or buffer stops). There may be a train on the line ahead so be ready to stop short of it.

Shunt-ahead Signals:
Proceed for shunting purposes only.

In each case the main stop signal arm will remain at danger.

Shunting signals are usually fixed near the ground and take the form of a white disc or small arm. The disc has a red stripe, which is horizontal in the normal (stop) position. The small arm is also horizontal for stop, and a red or white light is displayed at night. The proceed indication is given by the disc being rotated or the arm being pivoted up or down through approximately 45°, with

a green light at night. In this case, 'proceed' applies only as far as the line is clear.

A few shunting signals have a black disc with a yellow stripe, or a yellow arm, especially where shunting movements pass to and fro over a set of points normally lying in a particular direction. The signal may be ignored in such circumstances, but if a movement is to be made over the points when they have been turned to the other direction the signal must be obeyed.

Junction Stop Signals (Geographic or Otherwise)
The positioning and stepping of signals is as follows (see sketch):

Signal 1 applies to the straight route.
Signal 2 applies to the diverging route to the left.
Signal 3 applies to the diverging route to the right.

The vertical arrangement is normally used only for shunting signals.

Where speeds are low, eg in station areas, only one signal is provided in some cases, and the route is indicated by a figure or letter near to the signal arm.

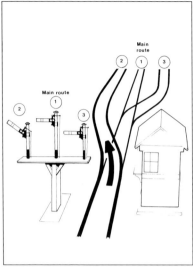

Above: A junction signal (horizontally arranged).

Below: A fine example of an ex-Great Western Railway junction signal at Worcester Shrub Hill. The distant signal arms are fixed in the caution position. *D. C. Hall*

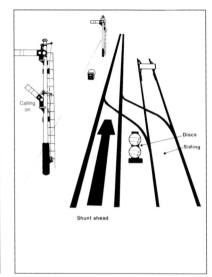

Above: Subsidiary and shunting signals showing the ground disc shunting signals. These are often grouped one above the other. In such cases the top disc normally reads to the route on the extreme left, and so on.

Below: Junction signal in a low-speed area.

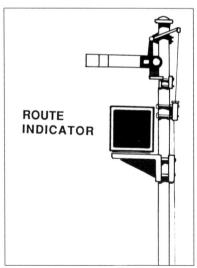

ROUTE INDICATOR

Banner Repeating Signals
A banner repeating signal consists of a small black semaphore arm (square-ended for stop signals and fish-tail-ended for distant signals) in a frame. They are provided on the approach to signals to assist the driver in those cases where the sighting of the main signal is restricted, eg by curvature of the line, or by buildings, tunnels, etc. The banner arm is always in the same position (horizontal or turned through 45°) as the main signal arm to which it applies.

Above: A three-direction signal gantry at Kilmarnock in 1973, showing the three possible routes ahead of the signals *Derek Cross*

Below: A now-rare example of a four-disc shunting signal at Forders Sidings. The top disc leads to the route on the extreme left, the second disc to the second-left, and so on. *D. C. Hall*

13: Absolute Block Lines — Arrangement of Signals and Track Circuits at Stations and Junctions. Locking and Controls

The following sketches show the typical arrangement of signals at a station and a junction:

At a Station
The names of the signals are as follows:

1 Up Distant.
   Cannot be cleared until 2 and 3 have been cleared.
2. Up Home (stop).
   Cannot be cleared if 3 is at clear. It is also the outermost stop signal.
3. Up Starting (stop).
   Cannot normally be cleared unless the block indicator at 'Z' is at the 'Line clear' position. This signal may also be referred to in some circumstances as the platform

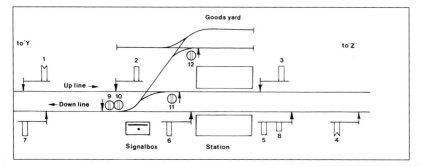

Above: **Typical arrangement of signals at a station.**

starting signal. It is sometimes referred to as the Up Section signal, because it allows access to the Up Section.

4. Down Distant.
Cannot be cleared until 5, 6 and 7 have been cleared.

5. Down Home No 1 (stop).
Cannot be cleared if 6 or 7 are at clear. It is also the outermost stop signal.

6. Down Home No 2 (stop).
Cannot be cleared if 7 is at clear. It may also be referred to as the platform starting signal in some circumstances.

7. Down Starting (stop).
Cannot normally be cleared unless the block indicator at 'Y' is at the 'Line clear' position. It may also be referred to as the Down Section signal.

8. Calling-on.
Allows a second train to enter the platform (eg for connecting purposes). The signal must not be cleared until the train has stopped or nearly stopped at it, in order to ensure that the train proceeds into the station at very low speed.

9. Shunting.
Setting back Down Main to Up Main.

10. Shunting.
Setting back Down Main to Sidings.

11. Shunting
Setting back Up Main to Down Main.

12. Shunting
Sidings to Down Main.

The points and signals are interlocked so that the signals can only be cleared when the points are in the corresponding position.

At a Junction

The names of the signals are as follows:

1. Up Distant.
Can only be cleared for the straight route to 'Z'. This ensures that the driver reduces speed for the junction turnout if proceeding to 'Y'. Occasionally an arm may

be provided for each route (Splitting Distants).

2. Up Home to 'Y'.

3. Up Home to 'Z'.

4. Up Starting to 'Y'.

5. Down Distant from 'Y'.

6. Down Outer Home from 'Y'.
This is an additional signal, ¼mile from No 7, which allows the signaller to accept a train from 'Y' whilst the signals have been cleared for a train to or from 'Z'.

7. Down Inner Home from 'Y'.

8. Down Starting.

9. Down Distant from 'Z'.

10. Down Outer Home from 'Z' This is an additional signal, ¼ mile from No 11, which allows the signaller to accept a train from 'Z' whilst the signals have been cleared for a train from 'Y'.

11. Down Inner Home from 'Z'.

12. Up Starting to 'Z'.

The sequential locking of signals, and the interlocking of points and signals, are as shown under the heading 'At a Station'.

The Starting signals are sometimes referred to as the Section signals.

Track Circuits

Track circuits are provided where traffic and other considerations justify it. A typical arrangement, based on the station sketch, would be:

Station limits (between signals 2 and 3 on the Up line; 5 and 7 on the Down line) are fully track-circuited, but divided into several separate sections. The track circuits, when occupied, have the following effects:

TC A/TC D
These are known as berth track circuits. They ensure

41

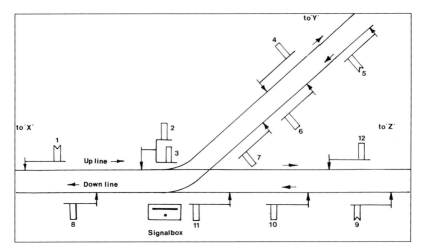

that a train is safely protected when standing at the home signal, by electrically locking the block indicator at 'Train on line'. This in turn ensures that the signallers at 'Y' and 'Z' cannot clear their starting signals to allow another train to approach. Furthermore, the block indicator for the rear section cannot be released until the train has occupied and cleared these track circuits. This ensures that the signaller cannot inadvertently release the block indicator for the rear section whilst there is still a train in it.

TC B
Locks signal 2 at danger and locks the points.

TC C
Locks signal 2 at danger.

TC E
Locks signal 5 at danger.

Above: Typical arrangement of signals at a junction.

Below: Typical arrangement of track circuits at a station.

TC F
Locks signal 6 at danger and locks the points.

TC G
Locks signal 6 at danger.

One of the main features of such track circuits is that they guard against the possibly disastrous consequences of the signaller forgetting about a train or locomotive standing in his station limits. They also prevent points from being moved under a train.

TCs A and D also perform another function. The block indicators at 'Y' and 'Z' electrically lock at danger signals

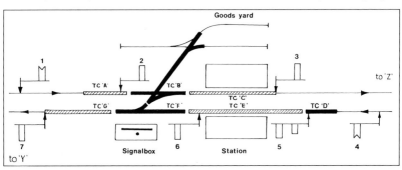

42

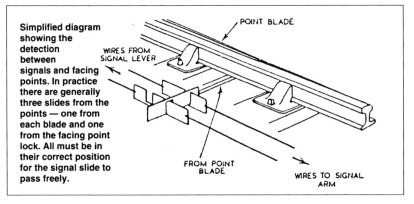

Simplified diagram showing the detection between signals and facing points. In practice there are generally three slides from the points — one from each blade and one from the facing point lock. All must be in their correct position for the signal slide to pass freely.

POINT BLADE

WIRES FROM SIGNAL LEVER

FROM POINT BLADE

WIRES TO SIGNAL ARM

2 and 5, and the signals are only released either when the block indicator is moved to 'Line clear' or when a train occupies those track circuits. This ensures that signals 2 and 5 cannot be cleared until the train is slowing down ready to stop at the signal, unless it has already been accepted by 'Y' or 'Z'. Without such an arrangement a driver might see the home signal at clear some distance away and overlook the starting signal at danger, causing the train to enter the section ahead without having been accepted by the signaller.

It can be seen that berth track circuits A and D perform several vital safety functions, but there is yet another. If a train should occupy a berth track circuit when, owing to some misunderstanding between the signallers, it had been allowed to enter the rear section without the block instrument having been placed at 'Train on line', the block instrument would immediately move to 'Train on line' as a safety measure. When a train first occupies a berth track circuit, a buzzer (known as an annunciator) will sound if the home signal is at danger, to draw the signaller's attention to the fact and inform him that he may now clear the signal if conditions ahead allow (and always provided that the signaller is satisfied that the speed of the train has been suitably reduced).

Three other safety controls might be mentioned:

Sequential Locking
The signal levers are interlocked and must be pulled off (ie cleared) in a predetermined order. Referring to the station sketch, the order would be:

Up Line	Down Line
1. Home signal (No 2)	1. Home No 1 signal (No 5)
2. Starting signal (No 3)	2. Home No 2 signal (No 6)
3. Distant signal (No 1)	3. Starting signal (No 7)
	4. Distant signal. (No 4)

The distant signal must be replaced first, but the stop signals can be replaced in any order.

Above: **Mechanical detector at facing points.**

Home Normal Contact
There is electrical locking between the home signal lever and the block indicator for the rear section, which ensures that the block indicator cannot be moved to the 'Line clear' position unless the home signal lever is back in the frame in the normal position, with the signal at danger. It compels the signaller to restore all signals to danger after the passage of each train.

Distant Arm Proving
The position of the distant signal arm (ie caution or clear) is indicated on an instrument in the signalbox and electrically interlocked with the block indicator in such a manner that the block indicator cannot be moved to the line clear position unless the distant signal arm is at caution.

Note — not all the safety controls described in this chapter are provided in every signalbox. Their provision depends on the number and speed of trains, the importance of the line, etc.

Use of Colour Light Signals in Absolute Block Signalling
For many years it has been the practice to replace isolated semaphore distant signals with a colour light signal which can show a yellow or a green light. Colour lights show up more clearly in the dark, and no special precautions are necessary during fog or falling snow. The clearing point is 200yd.

Occasionally the home signal itself may be replaced by a colour light signal, in which case it will have three aspects — red, yellow and green. It will show a yellow aspect if the starting signal is at danger, and the distant

43

Left: **A facing point bolt.**
IAL

signal may be modified to show two yellow lights. This arrangement only applies where certain distance criteria are met.

Finally, the starting signal may be replaced by a colour light signal, in which case it will have two aspects — red and green.

The use of colour light signals in this way can be especially convenient where the sections are short, and the distant signals for one signalbox are mounted underneath the stop signals of the signalbox in rear, on the same post. Incidentally, in the latter case the distant and stop signal arms are mechanically 'slotted' together, so that the distant signal cannot show 'clear' when the stop signal is at danger.

Safety at Points

Measures must be taken to ensure that facing points are lying in the correct position for the safety of an approaching train. (Facing points are those which can change the direction of a train approaching them. For trains coming the other way they are known as trailing points.) This is achieved in a number of ways:

1. Interlocking between the levers operating the points and signals, so that a wrong signal cannot be cleared.
2. Detection on site between the point blades and the signal. A slotted bar runs at right angles from each point blade to a detector. When the points are fitting correctly another slotted bar in the wire operating the signal is able to slide through at a right angle in the detector. This ensures that the points are fitting correctly and only the correct signal can be cleared. (See sketch.)
3. To guard against danger in the event of the signaller inadvertently replacing the signal to danger and

Left: **Canonbury Junction, 1979. Note the trailing trap points in the branch line, to protect the main line.**
Les Bertram

44

moving the points as the train is about to pass over them, or is actually doing so, a long pivoted bar is fixed to the inside of one of the rails immediately preceding the point. This bar is operated by a lever in the signalbox and, when the lever is moved, the bar swings up to rail level, an operation which is physically impossible when the flange of a wheel is pressing down on the bar. In many cases the bar has been replaced by a track circuit which, when occupied, locks the lever which locks the points.

4. The points are physically secured by a bolt or plunger which passes through a hole in a bar connecting the two point blades. The bolt is worked by a lever in the signalbox, which is interlocked with the signal levers. The bolt cannot be withdrawn when the signal is at clear, nor can the signal be cleared unless the bolt is detected as being through the hole in the bar connecting the two point blades. (See photograph of a facing point lock.)

5. An automatic time release (known as a back lock) on signals protecting points.

One other piece of apparatus ought to be mentioned — the fouling bar. When a train has passed through a facing point, the last vehicle has to proceed sufficiently far beyond the junction before a following train can pass safely through the junction to the other route. The precise spot to which the line beyond the facing points must be clear is known as the 'fouling point' and sometimes in station areas a spring-loaded bar, known as a depression bar, may be fixed to the inside of the rail up to the fouling point. The wheel flange of any vehicle standing on the depression bar presses it down and operates an electrical contact which locks the signals concerned. In calculating the required length of the depression bar, regard must be paid to the maximum possible overhang at the ends of vehicles and the distance between the inside wheel-sets of bogies. The same effect can be obtained by the use of track circuits.

14. Absolute Block Lines — Working of Semaphore Signals and the Acceptance of Trains

Acceptance of Trains

Under Absolute Block Regulation 3.4 a train may only be accepted by a signaller during clear weather when the following conditions are met:

1. The line is clear to the clearing point (200yd beyond the home signal if the distant signal is a colour light signal; 440yd if the distant signal is a semaphore). This is a safety overlap.

2. All points between the home signal and the clearing point are correctly set and locked for the safety of the approaching train.

3. No conflicting movement has been authorised which

will cross or foul the safety overlap.

4. No other train has been accepted whose acceptance required any portion of that safety overlap. In other words, once a safety overlap has been 'promised' to a train, it cannot be promised to another at the same time.

In normal circumstances, after a train has been accepted, the line on which it will run must be kept clear until either the train has stopped at the home signal or it has passed beyond any points which require to be used within the safety overlap or its journey has been cancelled.

Acceptance During Fog or Falling Snow — Additional Conditions

1. If the distant signal is a colour light and the home signal a semaphore, the safety overlap is 440yd.

2. If the distant signal is a semaphore, the advance section must also be clear, together with the safety overlap of the signalbox in advance. To enforce this, a train must not be accepted unless the 'Train out of section' bell signal has been received from the signalbox in advance and the block indicator for the advance section is in the normal (Line blocked) position. This is known as 'double-block' working.

3. If the home signal of the signalbox in advance is less than half a mile from the signalbox in rear, then, as an additional safety measure, the train must have been accepted by the signaller in advance before it can be accepted from the rear signaller. To clarify this, let us take three signalboxes, A, B and C. Before B can accept a train from A he must have had it accepted by C.

4. If a train in classes 1 to 6 has to be allowed to approach with the facing points set for an unbooked route which is speed-restricted, the signaller in rear must be told, and the train must be accepted in accordance with the restricted acceptance Regulation 3.5 and not with the normal acceptance Regulation 3.4. The term 'unbooked' means a route not shown in the Working Timetable or in any supplement or in the Weekly Special Traffic Notice.

Restricted Acceptance (Regulation 3.5)

This regulation is used only where specified in the Absolute Block Regulations or at specially authorised signalboxes. In the latter case the line need be clear only to the home signal, but the safety overlap may be obstructed. This Regulation is not normally allowed to be used during fog or falling snow.

To accept a train under Reg 3.5 the 'Is line clear' signal must not be repeated back, but the 'Restricted acceptance' signal (3-5-5) must be sent instead. The signaller in rear will acknowledge this signal by repetition, after which the block indicator may be moved to 'Line clear'. If, before the train enters the section, the acceptance circumstances change to permit the train to

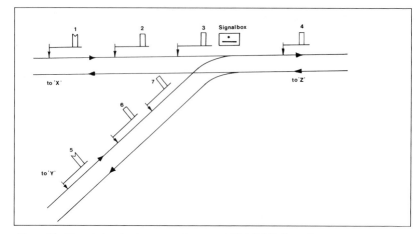

Above: **Working of signals at a converging junction (see text).**

be accepted under Reg 3.4 in the normal way the bell signal 'Line now clear in accordance with Reg 3.4 for the train to approach' (3-3-5) must be sent.

If the section signal at the signalbox in rear cannot be cleared because it requires a 'Line clear' release which in turn cannot be given because the block indicator is held at 'Train on line' by the occupation of a track circuit in the safety overlap, the driver, when being cautioned about the restricted acceptance, will be authorised to pass the section signal at danger.

Where engineering work is taking place within the clearing point, a train may only be accepted under the Restricted Acceptance arrangements and the driver must be told why.

Working of Signals at Converging Junctions
Signals 2 and 6 are additional (or outer) home signals to allow trains to be accepted from X and Y simultaneously. They are at safety overlap distance from signals 3 and 7, which become inner home signals. The outer home signal must not be cleared for a train from X when the signals have been cleared for a train from Y, but the train from X must be held at the outer home signal No 2. Also vice versa.

Train Out of Section Signal
The 'Train out of section' signal (2-1) must be sent and the block indicator placed to the normal position when the train has cleared the safety overlap. The signaller must ensure that there is a tail light/lamp on the last vehicle, as an assurance that no part of the train has been

accidentally left in the section.

At signalboxes where the use of the Restricted Acceptance arrangement is in operation the 2-1 bell signal should be sent as soon as the train has passed the home signal and whilst it is still in the safety overlap (provided the class of train is suitable, ie normally a freight train), but the block indicator must be maintained at 'Train on line' until the safety overlap is clear, whereupon it must be moved to normal and one beat on the bell sent. Signallers normally use discretion and apply this procedure only if the train concerned is likely to occupy the safety overlap for more than the normal time.

If the train is shunted or diverted clear of the main line before it passes the signalbox and the signaller does not see the tail lamp, he must not send the 'Train out of section' signal until a member of the traincrew has told him that the train is complete. Where such movements occur frequently, a telephone is normally provided to enable the traincrew to speak to the signaller.

Working of Signals When the Train is not Accepted by the Signaller in Advance
When a signaller offers a train to the signaller in advance, but it is not accepted, he works his signals in a special way to reinforce the fact that the starting signal is at danger. If the driver were to miss the starting signal and wrongly proceed into the next section, a collision could result.

The signaller will keep all his signals at danger until the train has nearly stopped at the home signal, then he will clear it (slowly, in practice, but not by rule) and allow the train forward. There is an exception to this Rule where the stop signal in rear of the signal at danger is a colour light signal which can display a yellow aspect (special conditions apply).

Where there is a berth track circuit (usually 200yd

long) preceding the home signal, the signaller may clear the home signal as soon as the berth track circuit is occupied, provided he is satisfied that the train is slowing down to stop at the signal. This proviso is important.

The driver will draw forward slowly past the home signal and will understand that the next stop signal ahead may be at danger. He will keep an eye on the signalbox to see if the signaller is holding out a red flag or light, in which case the driver must stop there because the signaller requires to tell him something, which may be a cautionary instruction about the state of the line ahead. If the driver is stopped at the signalbox, he must not restart his train until the signaller has held out a green handsignal. If the driver has been instructed to pass a signal at danger, a yellow handsignal is given instead of a green one.

Complications arise when the signaller cannot tell whether the starting signal is at danger or not. It may be out of sight and he may have no repeater. In such circumstances the train must be held at the signal in rear unless the driver can be told about it. During fog or falling snow a train must not be allowed to draw forward to a semaphore section signal (formerly known as a Starting Signal) to await acceptance, in case the driver misses the signal altogether.

Replacing Signals to Danger or Caution

The normal position of signals is danger, or caution in the case of distant signals. A distant signal must be replaced to caution as soon as the signaller can tell that the whole train has passed the signal. A stop signal must be replaced to danger as soon as the last whole train has passed it, except that where there are facing points beyond that signal the signaller must wait until the last vehicle has passed those points before he replaces the signal to danger.

Once the signaller has cleared his signals for a train he must not, except in emergency, replace them to danger until the train has either passed or stopped at them. (There is an exception to this at junctions when the

wrong priority has been given, but the signals may only be replaced to danger if the train is sufficiently far away.)

If a signal is at 'clear' for a train to start (eg from a station) and the signaller requires to replace it to danger before the train does start, he must make sure that the driver knows about it before the signal is replaced and the line ahead is obstructed or points are moved. This is to guard against the danger of the driver failing to check that the signal is still at clear before he moves off.

After operating a lever the signaller must look to see (where he can) that the signal or points have moved correctly. If a repeater is provided, he must check such operation by reference to the repeater, where necessary. He must use the wire adjusters provided to cater for variations in temperature.

The signaller must watch the track circuit indicators during the passage of trains, as far as practicable.

Working of Signals at Diverging Junctions

If a train in classes 1 to 6 is to be diverted from its booked route at a junction over which speed must be reduced, the junction signal must not be cleared until the train is close to it and, where practicable, the signaller is satisfied that its speed has been suitably reduced (not applicable if approach release arrangements are in operation). The term 'booked route' means the route shown in the Working Timetable, or in any supplement or in the Weekly Special Traffic Notice. During fog or falling snow the restricted acceptance arrangements apply (Reg. 3.5).

If the signaller cannot set the junction points until the train is close to the junction signal, he must as far as practicable ensure that it is safe to do so, having regard to the position and speed of the train.

Working During Fog or Falling Snow

Instructions for working during fog or falling snow apply as soon as the fog marking point, normally a nominated signal, becomes obscured. If a fog marking point is not specified at a signalbox, a distance of 200yd will apply.

Right: The operating floor of Mill Hill signalbox, unusually arranged in two separate frames. The left-hand frame controls the Slow lines, and the right-hand frame the Fast lines. The 'Rotary Block' instruments and other equipment are of the ex-Midland Railway pattern. The signalbox was photographed in 1954 and is now replaced by West Hampstead power signalbox. *IAL*

During severe frost the signaller must frequently work his signals, points, etc, to prevent them from freezing up.

When a train has to be stopped by signals, eg because it has not been accepted by the signaller in advance, the signaller must, if practicable, place a detonator on the rail to warn a driver who may have failed to see the home signal at danger. Detonator-placing machines are provided at most signalboxes, worked by a lever or handle in the signalbox itself, and can be used for this purpose. They are also available for use in any emergency, whether in clear or foggy weather.

15. Absolute Block Lines — Inside the Signalbox. Equipment to Help the Signalman

Signalboxes are normally constructed with two storeys, the signaller being located on the upper floor to give him a better all-round view. The lower floor contains technical equipment. However, before we enter the signalbox we should observe the notice on the door which says 'Private' or 'No Admittance'. The signaller must not allow unauthorised people to enter.

The two main features of the interior of the signalbox are the frame containing all the levers and the shelf above it carrying all the block instruments, bells, tappers, repeaters, etc.

The levers are grouped for convenience, those most frequently used being towards the centre of the frame. Each lever has a locking catch or handle to secure its position in the frame. Levers are referred to as being 'reversed' when pulled over, and 'replaced' when put back. They are painted in different colours for different functions, eg stop signals — red; distant signals — yellow; points — black. Levers which are electrically locked by the block indicators have a white band. If the signal is a colour light, or if the points are power-worked, the lever handle is cut short by six inches as a reminder to the signalman that little or no effort is needed to reverse the lever. Each lever is numbered and has a

nameplate, which may bear the numbers of any levers that are interlocked with it.

When a signaller operates a lever, he must check that the signal or points concerned have gone to the correct position, either by direct observation, or by observing the appropriate indicator in the signalbox.

The block shelf carries the electrically-operated instruments, such as:

1. The block instruments. In some cases there may be one for each line and each direction. In other cases the block indicators for both directions on a pair of lines to and from the same signalbox may be combined in one instrument. Block instruments usually have three indications, known as positions — (1) Normal or Line blocked, (2) Line clear, (3) Train on line. Block instruments in some parts of the country have reminder equipment attached. There may still be some older types of block instrument in use, dating back to pre-Grouping days, which differ from the above.

2. The bells, which convey coded messages from the signalboxes on each side. One bell is provided for each pair of lines to and from one signalbox, therefore at a junction on a four-track section with a two-track branch line there would be five bells, each one different in tone.

3. The tapper keys, for sending coded messages to, and acknowledging coded messages from, the signalboxes on each side. These keys are sometimes incorporated in the block instrument.

4. The block switch, which enables the signalbox to be closed when the line is still open for trains. When the signaller wishes to close he will send the appropriate bell signal to the next signalboxes (7-5-5) and turn the switch. This puts the signalboxes on each side into through communication with each other. He will then clear his signals. If the starting signal requires a 'Line clear' release he will send the bell signal 5-5-7 instead of 7-5-5. The signaller in advance will then move his

block indicator to 'Line clear' until he has been informed by one beat on the bell that the signal has been cleared, after which he will restore the block indicator to the normal position. A signaller may only switch out when there are no trains in the sections concerned and the block indicators are in the normal position.

After the Closing bell signal has been acknowledged, the signallers at each side of the box being switched out must test their indicators and bells. The signaller switching out must be told when all is in order and he must not leave duty until he has received this information.

5. Signal light repeaters. These instruments are provided for signals out of the signaller's sight and tell him whether the lights in the signals are in or out. When a light goes out, a buzzer will sound to alert the signaller, who will then take certain precautions regarding the movement of trains, and arrange to have the lamps relit. On those signals which are within his sight but have their backs to him, a small aperture, known as a back light, is cut in the back of the signal lamp and covered with plain glass so that the signaller can tell whether the lamp is alight or not. He can also tell whether the signal is on or off; when the signal is pulled off, a plate swings over and obscures the back light.

6. Signal arm repeaters. These instruments tell the signaller whether the arms of signals out of his sight are at danger or caution (on) or clear (off). There is an intermediate position, known as 'wrong', which indicates that the signal may be half-way between on and off, referred to by railwaymen as half-cock. Wire adjusters are provided so that the signaller can tighten or slacken the wire operating the signal and ensure that the signal is properly on or off.

7. Track circuit indicators. If the signalbox does not have an illuminated diagram incorporating the track circuit indications, separate instruments are provided for each track circuit, which indicate whether the track circuit is occupied or clear. The normal indicator takes the form of a centrally pivoted black or red rectangle in a white circle. The rectangle is horizontal when the track circuit is occupied, and rotates to 45° when the track circuit is clear.

8. Sealed releases. If an item of equipment fails and has the effect of locking points so that they cannot be moved (fail-safe mode) a release is provided in the form of a push-button so that the points can be moved under emergency conditions. The release button is normally covered by paper or glass, so that it cannot be pressed without tearing the paper or breaking the glass, which proves that it has been used. Once broken, the paper seal or glass can only be replaced by a qualified technician. Sealed releases must be

used with care by the signaller as they override the normal built-in safety of the interlocking.

Other equipment in the signalbox is as follows:

1. A large diagram, showing the track layout and all the points and signals under the control of the signaller. In some signalboxes, the track circuit indications are included on the diagram by means of coloured lights, in which case the diagram is referred to as an illuminated diagram.

2. A clock, which must be checked and corrected between 09.00 and 10.00 each day. On some lines a time signal is sent at 09.00 from a central point by means of a special code ring on the railway internal telephone circuit.

3. The train register book, in which all bell signals sent and received are recorded by time, to the nearest minute, half minutes being rounded up to the next minute. Details must be recorded of any unusual incident or engineering work. The signaller signs on and off in the train register book beneath the last entry.

4. Reminder appliances, which take the form of a metal collar or similar apparatus, to be slipped over a lever handle to remind the signaller not to pull over the lever in certain circumstances (and physically prevent him from doing so), eg in case of failure of equipment, or an obstruction on the line. Sometimes reminder appliances are provided which are slotted over the block instrument operating handle when a train is detained at the home signal or within the clearing point.

5. Detonators. These are small, round explosive devices which are fixed in an emergency to the top of the rail head by lead clips and are exploded by the wheels of a train passing over them, thus alerting the driver to any emergency. At most signalboxes detonators can be slid on to the rail head from a machine, operated by a lever or handle in the signalbox. These detonator placers can be effective even if the warning of an emergency is received by a signaller when a train is within a few yards of the signalbox. The detonators in the placers are changed on the first Monday of each alternate month.

6. Flags and lamps, for giving messages and instructions to drivers. There are three types of flag — green, yellow and red — but each lamp is capable of showing all three colours in rotation, together with a fourth, white, light.

7. Telephones connected to other signalboxes, offices, etc on a railway internal telephone circuit. Signalboxes usually have, additionally, a British Telecom telephone.

16. Intermediate Block Sections, Automatic Sections, Station Working, Ground Frames

Intermediate block is an economical means of dividing a block section into two separate sections, thus increasing line capacity. It is also a means of effecting economy by abolishing a signalbox which no longer has any function other than to signal trains straight along the main line. Intermediate block requires a stop signal roughly half-way between two signalboxes, together with an associated distant signal (see sketch).

Intermediate block is generally referred to by its initials 'IB'. In the sketch, the signaller would accept trains from 'Y' in the normal way and would clear his home and starting signals without asking for 'Line clear' from 'B' provided the line was clear to the overlap of the IB home signal. The line would be track-circuited throughout from 'A's starting signal to the end of the safety overlap beyond the IB home signal. When the signaller at 'A' wishes to clear the IB home signal he will offer the train to 'B' in the normal absolute block manner.

During fog or falling snow, if both the IB home and distant signals were semaphores, the signaller at 'A' would not clear his starting signal until he had received the 'Train out of section' signal from 'B' for the previous train, and the block indicator was at the normal position. However, most IB signals are colour light signals, in which case the above restrictions would not apply.

Automatic Sections

Automatic sections are a means of increasing line capacity, or of abolishing intermediate signalboxes without reducing line capacity. The line between the two signalboxes concerned is track-circuited throughout and may have one or more intermediate colour light stop signals, with associated colour light distant signals (see sketch).

In the sketch the signaller at 'A' would accept trains from 'Y' in the normal way. He would clear his starting signal as soon as automatic section No 1 was clear up to and including the overlap of the automatic stop signal. He would not offer the train to 'B', and the automatic stop signal would clear as soon as automatic section No 2, including overlap, was clear. He would, however, send the normal 'Is line clear' bell signal, so that the signaller at 'B' would know which class of train was approaching. In such a case, the 'Is line clear' signal would be regarded as a

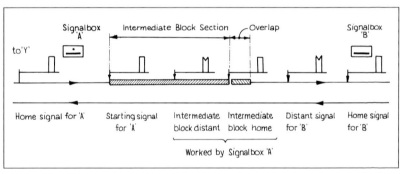

Above: Arrangement of signals and track circuits at an intermediate block section.

Below: Arrangement of signals and track circuits for an automatic section.

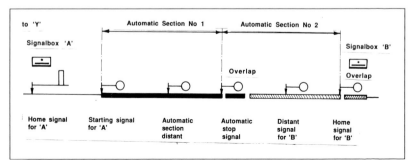

'Train description' signal. It will be appreciated that IB and automatic sections perform similar functions. Automatic sections are rather more expensive, because the line has to be track-circuited throughout.

Station Working

The Station Working regulations apply within station limits. Station limits extend from the outermost stop signal in rear to the most advanced stop signal (worked from the same signalbox) on the same line, and they separate the block sections from each other. In effect, the signaller is able to make shunting movements, propelling movements and wrong direction movements without special authority within his 'parish', but would require authority for such movements through or into a block section. However, before occupying the overlap with a movement which would come to a stand, he must send the 'Blocking back inside home signal' bell signal (2-4) to the signaller in rear, and after the signal has been acknowledged he must move the block indicator to 'Train on line'. If such a movement would occupy the line outside the home signal, ie in the rear block section, the bell signal 'Blocking back outside home signal' (3-3) is used instead. Certain conditions must be met before the signaller in rear gives permission for the movement to take place by acknowledging the signal. 'Blocking back' is a safety measure, as it requires the block indicator to be moved to 'Train on line', thus preventing the signaller from accepting another train in a moment of forgetfulness, when his safety overlap is not clear.

Ground Frames

Ground frames are provided to operate points in a running line which are too far distant from the signalbox to be worked in the normal way by rodding. The maximum distance for working points by rodding from the signalbox is 350yd. The points may be trailing ones giving access to a siding, or may form a trailing crossover. It is rare for facing points to be operated from a ground frame, except where provided to facilitate single line working.

A ground frame is usually an assembly of levers set in the open on a small wooden platform, with a telephone to the signalbox in rear. The levers are operated by a member of the traincrew or a shunter. (See page 2.)

The levers in the ground frame are locked in such a manner that they cannot be used unless certain conditions are fulfilled, and the usual method of operation is as follows (we will call the person operating the points a shunter, for convenience):

When the shunter wishes to operate the ground frame points he will telephone the signaller for permission. If the signaller is in a position to give such permission, depending on other train movements, he will release the ground frame by pulling over a lever, which in turn will lock his starting signal at danger. An indicator is provided at the ground frame to show whether it is locked or free, and when it shows 'free' the shunter will pull over a lever,

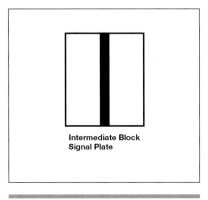

Intermediate Block Signal Plate

known as a king lever because when pulled over it releases the other levers in the ground frame through mechanical interlocking. The shunter is now free to carry out his shunting movements in safety.

When shunting is complete, the shunter will restore the points to normal, replace the king lever, and telephone the signaller accordingly.

At some ground frames, the whole train may be set back into the sidings clear of the main line, and in order to ensure safety a track circuit is provided on the main line covering a distance of a maximum train length plus 100yd on the approach side of the ground frame points and extending to 200yd beyond the points. A stop signal may also be provided on the main line, just before the points. It is normally at clear.

The track circuit controls the release as follows:

1. For a rightaway movement from the siding to the main line, the track circuit must be clear.
2. For a setting-back movement from the main line into the sidings, the track circuit must be occupied for a sufficient time to ensure that the train has come to a stand.

This section of Chapter 16 describes the normal arrangements at ground frames, but they may differ in detail at some individual ground frames, especially where they have been in use for many years.

17. How Emergencies are Dealt With on Absolute Block Lines

The arrangements for dealing with all types of emergencies and irregularities on absolute block lines have been developed and refined over more than a century, usually to incorporate lessons learned from accidents, and they are voluminous. The details given in this chapter are meant as a general guide and summary, and are not intended to be comprehensive.

The term 'guard' is synonymous with 'conductor', etc.

The following types of emergency are dealt with in this chapter:

- An obstruction on the line.
- A train needing to be stopped for examination owing to a defect, etc.
- A train taking an unusually long time to pass through a section.
- A train passing without a tail lamp.
- Protection of the line.
- Dealing with a train which has broken down in the section.
- Examination of the line.
- Failure of the block signalling equipment.

An Obstruction on the Line

If a signaller becomes aware of an obstruction on the line which might endanger a train, and the obstruction is either in the rear section or in his safety overlap, he must send the 'Obstruction danger' signal (six beats) to the signaller in rear, and move his block indicator to 'Train on line' (if it is not already in that position). He must also place or maintain his signals at danger to protect the obstruction. The 'Obstruction danger' signal must also be sent if it is necessary to prevent the approach of a train from the box in the rear for any other exceptional cause.

He must also send six beats if he sees a train approaching which he has not accepted, or for which he has not received the 'Train entering section' signal; this enables trains to be stopped whilst the situation is investigated and rectified.

The signaller must then inform the other signaller of the reason for sending the signal.

The signaller receiving six beats must immediately take the following action:

1. Put his signals to Danger if they have been cleared.
2. Operate his detonator-placing machine, where provided.
3. Put three detonators on the obstructed line, 20yd apart. (Usually, in signalboxes which are open continuously, they are hung on a nail near the door for just such an emergency.)
4. Acknowledge the six beats.
5. Answer the telephone. The other signaller will be telephoning to say why he sent six beats.
6. If he succeeds in stopping a train which is proceeding towards the obstruction he must send the 'Cancelling' signal (3-5). If he is not successful he must at once, without acknowledging the six beats and without sending 'Call attention', send the 'Train running away' signal (4-5-5). The signaller in advance, on receiving the 4-5-5 signal, must do everything he can to stop

the approaching train before it hits the obstruction, but there is often little that he can do in the time available.

Animals on the line are not considered to be a sufficient obstruction to justify sending the 'Obstruction danger' signal, but all trains must be stopped so that the drivers can be told about the situation and instructed to proceed cautiously. The train must not enter a tunnel until it has been established that there are no animals in it.

If a driver or guard sees a cow or bull or other large animal within the boundary fence, irrespective of whether trains are immediately in danger or not, or if either person sees other animals on or near the track and considers that trains may be endangered, he must alert the signaller. The driver must warn the driver of any approaching train by sounding the horn and showing a red light. The driver must also stop his train and place a track circuit operating clip and three detonators on the other line, at least 1¼ miles from the animals, except where the signaller has been contacted and has given assurances that it is not necessary.

A Train Needing to be Stopped for Examination Owing to a Defect, etc

A signaller is required to watch each train as it passes, to see whether everything is in order. If anything unusual is seen, such as signals of alarm, goods displaced dangerously or falling off, fire, a hot axlebox, a door open, a divided train, etc, he must stop the train if he can, but if not he must send the 'Stop and examine train' signal (seven beats) to the signaller in advance, and telephone him with the reason. This action must also be taken if the signaller becomes aware that the train may have caused damage to the infrastructure. He must also stop trains going the other way unless he is satisfied that there is no need to do so.

The signaller receiving seven beats must put all his signals to danger for both directions, and when the train arrives it must be dealt with as necessary. If nothing can be found, the driver of the next train through the section concerned on any line must be told about it, instructed to proceed cautiously and report at the next signalbox.

If something is found which cannot be dealt with there and then, the train may be sent forward to a place where it can be dealt with. Whilst being worked forward in this manner, the train must not be passed by another train running on an adjacent line unless it has been established that it can be done safely.

If a signaller sees a door open on a passenger train but there is no report of anyone having fallen from the train, he must tell the signaller in rear, so that the driver of the first train through the section on each line can be sent through at caution, having been instructed to keep a good lookout. If, however, there is definite information that a passenger has fallen from the train, all trains must be detained until the line has been examined.

If the signaller notices or is told that a train is

proceeding without a headlight being shown, he must arrange for the driver to be made aware. It is better for this to be done at the next signalbox rather than bring the train to a sudden stand.

Train in Section for an Unusually Long Time

If a signaller receives the 'Train entering section' signal for a train, which then fails to appear at the appropriate time, it is obvious that something is wrong. The train may merely be proceeding more slowly than usual, but on the other hand it may have broken down or, worse still, it may have collided with an obstruction or become derailed. There are many reasons why the train may have stopped and it is important to find out what has happened. It is also important to stop any other train from proceeding into the section until the driver has been appraised of the situation and instructed to proceed cautiously. During poor visibility, or if there is a tunnel in the section, the line must first be examined (see below) before trains are allowed to run.

The signaller must not accept a train on any line in the same direction until he has told the signaller in rear what has happened. However, if he has already accepted a train but it has not yet entered the section, he must send the 'Train an unusually long time in section' signal (6-2).

Eventually the signaller will discover what has happened, either from a member of the traincrew walking to the nearest signalbox or telephoning, or from the driver of the first train passing cautiously through the section. Appropriate action can then be taken.

A Train Passing Without a Tail Lamp

Every train carries on the last vehicle either a detachable tail lamp, or a built-in tail lamp, displaying a red light, in order to prove that it is complete and that part of the train has not been left in the section through some mischance. The signaller must observe the tail lamp/light before he sends the 'Train out of section' signal. When loose-coupled trains (ie trains without continuously-coupled power brakes) were common, they not infrequently broke in two with the rear portion coming to a stand in mid-section and the front portion continuing forward unchecked. It was vital that the signaller became aware of this, through the absence of a tail lamp at the rear of the first portion. If a continuously-braked train breaks in two, the parting of the brake pipe will normally cause the brakes to be applied automatically, bringing both portions to a stand, possibly in mid-section. However, just in case the brakes should fail to be applied on the first portion, it is still important for the signaller to look out for the tail lamp.

If a train is seen to pass without a tail lamp, it must be stopped as soon as reasonably practicable. Any train going the other way must also be stopped and the driver must be told what has happened and that he must proceed cautiously. The signaller noticing the absence of a tail lamp must send the 'Train passed without tail lamp' signal (nine beats to the signaller in advance, 4-5 to the signaller in rear) and maintain the block indicator at 'Train on line'. During poor visibility, or if there is a tunnel in the section, the line must first be examined (see below) before trains are allowed to run.

If a train passes with the tail lamp on but out when it should be lit, no special action is necessary by the signaller other than to send nine beats to the next signaller and tell him why.

The signaller receiving nine beats must stop the train concerned if he can do so without bringing it to a sudden stand, then find out whether it is complete or not, and take appropriate action. If stopping the train would cause it to brake suddenly it must be allowed to proceed, in which case the signaller concerned must pass forward the 'Train passed without tail lamp' signal.

Protection of the Line

It might be appropriate here to say a few words about the actions of traincrews when trains break down or have an accident in mid-section. In theory the train should be perfectly safe from any risk of another train running into the back of it, because the block signalling system should protect it, but there is always a remote risk that a signaller might make an error and allow another train to enter the section, which would be very dangerous.

However, an accident might obstruct another line, which will not at that moment be protected by the signalling system, and traincrews must take emergency action to secure what is known as 'The Safety of the Line'.

The driver must quickly decide whether any other line is obstructed and use the emergency call procedure to contact Operations Control by radio. He must also inform the signaller in the quickest way, either by radio or a nearby telephone. If he is unable to contact the signaller direct he must immediately carry out emergency protection, as follows:

He must place a track circuit operating clip on each line obstructed, display a red flag or light and place three detonators on the line, 20yd apart, 1¼ miles from the obstruction.

If the driver needs assistance in carrying out emergency protection on other lines, he must ask the guard or any other competent person to assist, but if the driver is unable to carry out protection (because he is injured or trapped, for example), the guard must carry out the driver's duties. The guard's first duties, therefore, are to place a track circuit operating clip on any obstructed line and then contact the driver. It is desirable for the guard to remain with the train and look after the passengers' welfare if this can be done without delaying protection.

The signaller's role when advised of a train accident is to put his signals to danger and arrange for a general emergency broadcast to be made by train radio.

This is a very general description of the arrangements for protection of the line, which are set out in great detail in Section M, (part i) of the Rule Book.

Dealing with a Train which has Broken Down in Section

If a train breaks down in mid-section, emergency protection need not be carried out except in certain circumstances when the driver is unable to contact the signaller immediately. However, some protection (known as 'Assistance Protection') is necessary to warn the driver of the assisting locomotive which is coming to move the broken-down train, that he is getting near to it. This special protection consists of three detonators, 20yd apart, 300yd from the train in the direction from which help is coming.

The driver must remain at the detonators, ready to conduct the driver of the assisting locomotive, and the signaller must not allow it to enter the section until he knows that the conductor driver is in his appointed place (or proceeding to it).

On a number of occasions an assisting locomotive has collided heavily with the broken-down train, so the instructions are now very precise:

The driver of the assisting locomotive must proceed very cautiously and look out for the driver of the failed train. The assisting driver must not enter a tunnel unless the failed train driver has been picked up or he is not in the tunnel. The assisting driver must stop on exploding the first detonators (which may be only 300yd from the train).

It will be noted that the guard is not involved in these arrangements. His duty is to remain with the train and look after the passengers.

So far as the signaller is concerned, he must tell the assisting driver the exact location of the failed train, how it is protected, and the point from where the failed train driver will conduct it. The assisting locomotive must not be allowed to enter the section until the signaller has sent the 'Train entering section' signal and had it acknowledged. After the failed train has been cleared from the section the next train on that line must also be sent through cautiously.

If the train which has broken down is cleared from the section either by being drawn back to the signalbox in rear, or by being hauled out at the signalbox in advance, there is a danger that part of it may accidentally have been left behind. To deal with that situation the block indicator must be maintained at 'Train on line', and the driver of the next train requiring to pass through the section on that line must be cautioned and told to pass the section signal at danger.

In this sub-section the term 'assisting locomotive' has been used for simplicity, but any type of train which is suitable may be used to clear from a section a train which has broken down. If there is no siding accommodation at

the signalbox in advance, the two trains may continue forward as far as necessary.

Examination of the Line

This must be interpreted in its widest sense of looking to see whether everything is safe for trains to proceed normally. The arrangements are very similar to those set out in Chapter 10 for track circuit block but the signalling of the train is somewhat different. The signallers concerned must be able to speak to each other, and the 'Train out of section' signal must have been received for the previous train. The signaller in rear does not send the 'Is line clear' signal for the examining train, but tells his colleague at the next signalbox what class of train it is, and sends only the 'Train entering section' signal. The driver of the examining train must be told by the signaller to pass the section signal at danger and proceed at caution.

Any class of train, including a passenger train, may be used to examine the line, and it is not necessary for the driver to be accompanied during darkness, fog or falling snow, nor if the affected portion of line is within a tunnel, unless the guard or other competent person is immediately available. However, the driver must not proceed through the tunnel at more than 10mph. If definite information has been received that someone has fallen from a train, the driver must be accompanied during darkness, fog or falling snow, or within a tunnel.

The arrangements for dealing with track circuit failures and suspected track defects are also very similar to those set out in Chapter 10 and need not be repeated here.

Failure of the Block Signalling Equipment

Occasionally the equipment will not work correctly, often owing to an interruption in the telegraph wire or cable between two signalboxes. When this happens, the failure may affect either the bells or the block instruments, or it may affect both. If a telephone is to hand, it may be used to pass signalling messages, but if telephone communication is not available, steps must be taken to obtain a replacement form of communication, eg radio. However, if the signaller can see that the section is clear, trains may be allowed to pass through. The 'Time Interval' method of working, which was in operation for many years, is no longer used.

Where only the bells have failed, but the block indicators are being worked in conjunction with telephone messages, the driver of the first train to pass through the affected section must be advised of the circumstances and instructed to proceed cautiously.

In all other cases, the signaller must advise the driver requiring to proceed into the section where the failure exists, of the circumstances, instructing him to pass the section signal at danger and proceed cautiously. The driver of the first train travelling on each adjacent line must be advised of the circumstances and told to proceed cautiously through the section.

PART 4

18. The Driver, the Guard and the Signals

Signals are the means by which the driver receives his instructions from the signaller. However, in addition to stop, caution and clear, there are other factors to be considered if safety is to be achieved.

Observance of Signals
When a train stops on the approach to a signal showing a proceed aspect (at a station platform, for example) the driver must look at the signal again before restarting in case the signaller has replaced it to danger in the meantime either in an emergency or to give priority to another train. In the latter case the signaller must not clear his signals for a conflicting movement until he is sure that the driver of the first train has noticed that the signal has been replaced.

If a driver finds a junction signal cleared for the wrong route he must stop at the signal if it is safe and practicable to do so, and speak to the signaller.

If a train is stopped, or nearly stopped, before the clearance of a stop signal (other than a multiple-aspect colour light), this may be a warning to the driver that the next signal may also be at danger. The signals are worked in this way in order to avoid any risk of the driver failing to observe the next signal, should it be at danger. When a train is stopped or nearly stopped in this manner the driver should also look to see if the signaller requires him to stop at the signalbox.

There may be locations where a position light signal or subsidiary semaphore signal is not provided for a permissive line, but in such cases the clearance of the main signal does not necessarily mean that the line ahead is clear. It is merely an authority to the driver to proceed, and he must be prepared to find the line ahead occupied. The driver needs to be aware from his route knowledge that this particular permissive move is possible, and how the signals present it to him.

Doubt as to Signal Aspect
In the following circumstances a driver must treat a stop signal as being at danger (or a distant signal at caution):

- No signal, where there should be one.
- No light in a signal (except for one which carries a white cross indicating that it is not in use).
- A colour light signal, where there is doubt as to which aspect applies.
- A semaphore signal at half-cock (neither on nor off). (After dark this may cause a part-green part-red light to be displayed.)

- A white light, where there should be a coloured light.

The driver must immediately inform the signaller, stopping specially to do so if necessary. He must also do so if he sees any irregularity in the working of signals, or an irregular aspect sequence, and complete the appropriate report form.

Being Authorised to Pass a Signal at Danger
There are several circumstances in which this may occur, the authority being given personally to the driver by the signaller or another nominated person. Before starting, the driver must reset the Driver's Reminder Appliance, give one long blast on the horn, then proceed cautiously at such reduced speed as will enable him to stop the train clear of any obstruction. The driver must always be able to stop within the distance he can see the line to be clear; it is better to incur delay than risk a collision or derailment by travelling too fast in the circumstances.

The driver must observe any facing points to see that they are in the correct position, and pass through them at not more than 15mph.

If the driver sees the next stop signal ahead showing a proceed aspect, he must not assume that it is meant for him. It may be for a train in front.

Train Detained at a Signal at Danger
A train standing at a signal could be in danger if its presence is forgotten by the signaller, unless a track circuit is provided. As a safeguard, therefore, if a track circuit is not provided the driver must go to the signalbox to remind the signaller that the train is there. The driver must also go to the signalbox if he is detained for an unusual time at a track-circuited signal. In colour light areas, although track circuits are provided, it is still necessary for the driver to speak to the signaller in case the latter wishes to give him a message.

The detailed requirements are as follows:

1. Where there is a telephone at the signal (indicated by a black and white diagonal striped sign) the driver must speak to the signaller within 2min, then at intervals of 5min if he is still detained. At some signals the driver is allowed to wait more than 2min before he makes his initial call, in which case the number of minutes is given on the black and white sign. At other signals, indicated by an '0' in a diagonally striped field, he is required to contact the signalman without delay.
2. Where there is a yellow diamond sign with the letter

'T' at the signal the driver need not speak to the signaller unless an associated white flashing light is displayed. This means, in effect, that the signaller has a message for the driver.

3. Where there is a yellow or white diamond sign with the letter 'X' at the signal, or where there is a sign showing a black cross on a white background with a yellow roundel superimposed on it on the telephone cabinet, the driver must not leave his cab to use the telephone except in emergency. He may use his radio but if there is not one available he must stay in his cab until the signal clears or until someone tells him that the next line has been blocked by the signaller and it is safe for him to leave his cab to use the phone. This procedure is in force at places where there are several running lines close together and the driver would be in danger if he left his cab to use the telephone.

4.1. If there is no telephone at the signal, the driver must sound the horn as soon as he comes to a stand. If there is a white diamond sign at the signal, the presence of the train is detected by a track circuit and there is no need for the driver to go to the signalbox immediately to remind the signaller about the train standing on the main line. However, if the train is detained for an unusually long time the driver must set off for the signalbox within 10min at the most.

4.2. If there is no white diamond sign at the signal, the driver must set off for the signalbox within 2min (immediately during fog or falling snow). When a section signal without a white diamond sign is at danger the driver must not draw down to stand at it, as he would then have to walk back to the signalbox to remind the signaller about the standing train, but he must stop his train as close as possible to the signalbox (well clear of any junction) so that the train is within the signaller's sight and the driver can reach the signalbox quickly and easily.

4.3 Where there is a white diamond sign with a telephone number displayed for NRN radio purposes, there is limited clearance beside the train and the driver must contact the signaller by radio.

Actions of Signaller and shunter

When a driver enters a signalbox to remind the signaller about his train standing on the main line, he must write in the train register book 'Train No . . . detained on . . . line at . . . signal', together with the time. Both men must sign the entry and the driver must remain in the signalbox to act as a reminder to the signaller, unless the signaller assures him that he has used his reminder appliances (eg by putting a lever collar on the signal in rear of the standing train).

Failure of Telephone at a Signal

If a train is detained at an automatic signal, or a semi-automatic signal, or an intermediate block home signal, and the driver finds that the telephone has failed, he must try to speak to the signaller by other means (eg from another telephone nearby) but if that is not practicable he must take his train past the signal at danger and proceed very cautiously to the next stop signal, taking special care at any points. He must then stop at the next signal, whether it is showing a proceed aspect or not, and try again to speak to the signaller. If unsuccessful he must repeat the above procedure at the types of signals mentioned, as many times as necessary. However, he must not pass a controlled signal in this manner.

At any other type of signal the driver must speak to the signaller the best way he can, but if it is not practicable for him to do so he must go to the signalbox.

If the train is detained at a controlled signal, the driver must contact the signaller by radio, or by using the telephone at another signal, or using a lineside telephone. If none of these is available, the driver must go to the signalbox. If he finds that signalbox closed he may proceed cautiously to the next signal or signalbox.

Left: **AWS receiver under the front bogie of an EMU.** *Author*

19. The BR Standard Automatic Warning System of Train Control, Known as AWS

This system was approved for use on BR in 1956, since when it has been installed on almost all main and suburban lines. Its simple purpose is to remind a driver that he needs to slow down or stop. If he fails to acknowledge such a reminder, the brakes will automatically be applied within two or three seconds. Most of Britain's total route mileage of approximately 10,000 has been equipped.

Track Equipment
A permanent magnet and an electro-magnet are installed between the rails (known as 'in the four-foot'), normally about 200yd on the approach side of signals which can display a caution or preliminary caution aspect. At certain locations a suppressible magnet may be provided beyond the signal.

A permanent magnet only is provided on the approach to speed restriction warning boards.

Locomotive or Multiple-unit Equipment
A receiver is fixed underneath the locomotive, and it

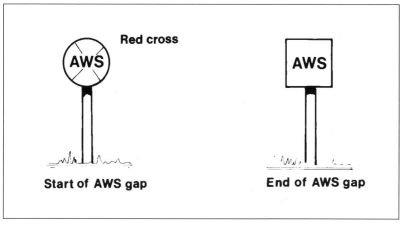

Above: Signs showing the start and finish of AWS gaps at a station.

Below: Signs showing the start and finish of AWS gaps for trains travelling in the wrong direction on a bi-directional line.

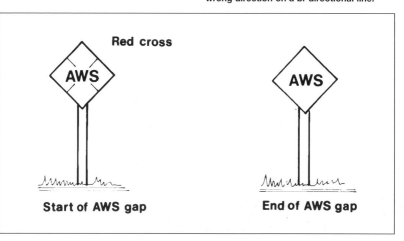

White cross blue background

Cancelling indicator used on single lines (denotes that AWS does not apply to trains travelling in that direction)

Above: **AWS cancelling indicator on a single line.**

reacts to the magnets fixed in the track. A bell and a horn (or an electronic representation) are provided in the cab, together with an acknowledgement button and a visual indicator.

Method of Operation

When a signal displays a clear aspect the electro-magnet is energised. This causes the bell in the driving cab to give a short ring, and the visual indicator to show all-black. No action is required by the driver.

In all other cases the electro-magnet is inoperative. When a locomotive passes over the permanent magnet the horn will sound a warning and unless the driver presses the acknowledgement button within two or three seconds (which will silence the horn) the brakes will be fully applied. The visual indicator will show all-black until the acknowledgement button is pressed, after which it will display a segmented disc, coloured alternately black and yellow, as a reminder to the driver that he has acknowledged a warning and that he has overridden the automatic brake application. The responsibility for applying the brake is now his.

Summary of Warnings

Where AWS equipment is provided, the warning horn will sound when the train is approaching the following:

1. A colour light signal displaying any of these aspects:
   • red
   • single yellow
   • double yellow
   • flashing single yellow
   • flashing double yellow.
2. A semaphore signal at caution.
3. A warning sign of a permanent speed restriction.
4. A warning sign of a temporary speed restriction.
5. A warning sign of a speed restriction imposed without notice in an emergency.
6. A cancelling indicator on a single or bi-directional line for trains moving in the opposite direction to which the signal applies.
7. A warning board in connection with two types of level crossing, where the train driver has to check that the flashing red road traffic signals are working properly before he takes his train over the crossing. These crossings are known as ABCL (automatic barrier crossing locally monitored) and AOCL (automatic open crossing locally monitored).
8. A signal displaying a clear aspect, alongside which has been placed a warning sign or indicator referring to a temporary or emergency speed restriction.
9. A splitting distant signal which is at clear for the lower speed route.

AWS Gaps

AWS equipment is often not provided at large stations where speeds are low, even though the approach lines are equipped. The start of the AWS gap is indicated by a circular white sign showing 'AWS' with a red cross. The end is indicated by a square white sign showing 'AWS'.

AWS equipment is sometimes not provided for trains travelling in the wrong direction on a bi-directional line. The start of the AWS gap is indicated by a diamond-shaped white sign showing 'AWS' with a red cross. The end is indicated by the same sign without the red cross.

Failures and Irregularities

If the bell sounds in circumstances in which the horn should sound (or if there is no sound), there is a misleading failure, known as a wrong-side failure, and the driver must tell the signaller at once, stopping specially if necessary, so that other drivers can be warned.

If there is a right-side failure (a horn, or no indication, when there should have been a bell) the driver must tell the signaller at the first convenient opportunity, so that the equipment can be examined.

AWS Isolation

A locomotive or unit must not enter service if the AWS is isolated (ie out of use) in any driving cab which is required to be used, or if the seal is broken on an AWS isolating handle. The meaning of the term 'In Service' has been amended to denote a train that is ready to start a journey. It no longer means entering service from a depot. A train is out of service at the end of a journey or reversing point. The term 'Journey' means a journey between a station (or depot or siding) and another station (or depot or siding). A journey finishes where a train has to reverse, or have vehicles attached or detached.

If, whilst in service, the pressing of the acknowledgement button does not stop the sounding of the horn, or does not prevent the brakes from being applied, the driver must isolate the AWS. He must then tell the signaller and not move the train until instructed to do so. The signaller must tell Operations Control at once.

The driver will be told of the arrangements which are being made. If a competent person is available to accompany the driver and stop the train in an emergency the train may proceed normally to a nominated point. If no such person is available, the train may proceed to a nominated point at a maximum speed of 40mph.

There are now very detailed and comprehensive instructions for dealing with AWS failures, following the Southall accident in 1997. They are contained in Sec H (part ii) of the Rule Book.

20. Automatic Train Protection

Automatic train protection, known as ATP, is an extension of the comparatively simple automatic warning system described in the previous chapter. AWS merely warns the driver when he needs to reduce speed or stop, either for a speed restriction or a signal at danger. It checks that the driver has actually received the warning, because unless he acknowledges the warning by pressing a button, the brakes will be applied automatically.

AWS, with its two-aspect safe/unsafe indication, was very suitable for absolute block signalling, and even with track circuit block and colour light signals it has been invaluable in raising safety standards on Britain's railways. However, it is not designed to check that the driver is actually responding to the warning he has acknowledged and that he is applying the brakes appropriately. It might be thought that such provision would be unnecessary, on the grounds that if a driver is sufficiently alert to acknowledge receiving the warning by the physical act of pressing a button, he is sufficiently alert to apply the brakes. However, there is now a substantial body of experience to show that this is not always the case, especially in circumstances where the AWS has to be cancelled several times at very short intervals. Several serious accidents have occurred in which drivers have pressed the acknowledgement button but have then failed to brake correctly, or even at all, and have gone past a danger signal. ATP is designed to cover that eventuality.

Two pilot schemes were introduced in 1991, from different manufacturers: one on the Great Western main

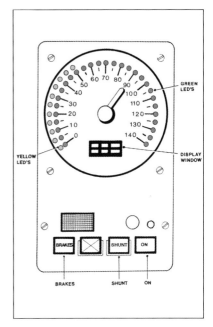

Above: ATP speedometer showing green LEDs and yellow LEDs around the periphery, and the display window.

lines between Paddington and Bristol, and a second on the Chiltern line from Marylebone. The trials were more technically demanding, costly and prolonged than was expected, and eventually it was decided in 1995 by the Secretary of State for Transport that ATP should not be extended to other routes on the grounds that the expenditure was not justified, ie that it would not be cost-effective. The system ought properly to be described as the BR-ATP system, as it differs in some respects from the subsequently developed European Train Control System (see Chapter 22). Attention was then concentrated on developing an enhanced form of BR-AWS under the name 'The Train Protection and Warning System', described in the next chapter.

Initially, BR-ATP works in a similar way to AWS. The train picks up messages from the track electronically, which may tell the driver when he needs to slow down or stop. However, the ATP system then goes on to check that the driver is actually reducing speed to the extent required. If it finds that he is failing to do so, it will remind the driver by giving a short visual and audible warning,

Left: **HST cab driver's console, showing AWS sunflower, ATP speedometer, brake control (left-hand black knob) and power control (right-hand black knob).** *Peter van der Mark*

and if that warning is unheeded by the driver, ATP will apply the brakes.

This backcheck is performed by an on-board computer which, on receipt of the warning, calculates the rate of deceleration (known as the braking curve) which will be required to bring the train safely to a stand at a danger signal (or reduce the speed to the level required by a speed restriction). The computer continuously checks the actual speed of the train against the braking curve which it has calculated, and gives a warning if it finds that the actual speed is higher than that demanded by the braking curve, followed if necessary by an application of the brake. A distance-measuring tachometer enables the computer to calculate the location of the train relative to the approaching signal.

ATP also safeguards the maximum permitted train speed throughout the journey by monitoring the actual train speed and checking it against the permitted speed. If the permitted speed is exceeded, ATP will intervene to cause speed to be reduced.

Track Equipment

At each signal, or at braking distance from a permanent speed restriction, transmitters called beacons or balises are laid in the track, and transmit the following information to the train via a receiver antenna fixed underneath the locomotive or unit:

- Distance to the next signal at danger or to a speed restriction.
- Current maximum permitted speed at the beacon.
- Value and length of next speed restriction, if there is one.
- The gradient of the track.
- Distance to the next balise.

Setting the On-board Computer

Certain information on board trains which does not alter their performance may be permanently programmed, eg the length and maximum permitted speed of a multiple-

unit. Only the driver identity number, the train length in number of coaches, and whether the system works in standard mode need be entered. In other cases, before starting the journey the driver will input the maximum permitted speed of the train, its type, length, weight and braking capability. All this information is input via a keyboard with LCD display. The information, together with that received from beacons, will enable the on-board computer to calculate the appropriate braking curve.

Cab Display

The main item of cab display is the ATP speedometer. Around the periphery of the dial are green light-emitting diodes (known as LEDs) at 5mph intervals, and one may be illuminated to show the maximum permitted speed, or flash to show a target speed ahead. Alongside these, from 0mph to 50mph, are yellow LEDs, which have a 'release speed' function. A display window in the speedometer, in the form of three matrix blocks of red LEDs, indicates free block sections ahead, and gives the driver a form of 'countdown' to a signal at danger.

Beneath the matrix blocks there are a number of buttons for purposes such as brake release after an intervention, passing a signal at danger with authority, shunting and setting up.

Method of Operation

When set up prior to departure the ATP display will show three dots (...) in the display window, which confirms that the system has been set up successfully. As soon as the train passes over the first beacon a green LED is illuminated next to the permitted speed and if the line ahead is clear, three characters (===) appear in the window.

When the train is approaching a double yellow signal, the green LED display, showing the maximum permitted speed, may change to a single flashing green LED at 0mph, and a short 'blip' tone will sound. The display window will show '0', meaning 'Stop at the next

Right: A close-up of the console in the previous picture showing the ATP speedometer left of centre.
Peter van der Mark

signal but two'. But normally, when the train passes the double-yellow signal, the display window will change to '00', meaning 'Stop at the next signal but one'. When the train passes the single-yellow signal, the display window will change to '000', meaning 'Stop at the next signal'.

Throughout this process, the train's actual speed will be compared with the braking curve calculated by the computer. If the driver fails to brake sufficiently, a warble tone will sound, the indicator in the display window will flash and the green LED will go out. If the driver allows the ATP system to interpose and apply the brakes, he cannot release them until speed has been reduced to 40mph.

So far as speed restrictions are concerned, the procedure is somewhat similar. Approaching a speed restriction, say 40mph, the steady green LED showing the maximum permitted speed will be replaced by a flashing green 40mph LED display, and a short 'blip' tone will sound. If the driver brakes correctly, the flashing LED will change to a steady 40mph display at the start of the speed restriction, and this indication will be maintained until the rear of the train has cleared the end of the speed restriction (hence the need for the driver to input the length of the train).

In order to carry out its functions without constantly interfering with the driver's handling of the train, the on-board ATP computer calculates three curves — the braking curve, the warning curve and the intervention curve. The warning curve, which gives a visual and audible warning to the driver when its speed is exceeded, has a tolerance of 3mph above the braking curve. Similarly, the intervention curve has a 3mph tolerance above the warning curve. The curves are calculated to achieve the required speed at the commencement of a speed restriction, or to bring the train safely to a stand in the case of a signal being at danger.

Track Equipment — Placed Intermittently or Laid Continuously

The main advantage of continuously-laid track equipment is that it will update the signal information the instant an aspect changes. This means that the driver can start to accelerate as soon as a signal ahead changes to a less restrictive aspect, even though he may not be able to see it. It also provides an added safeguard if a signal out of sight changes to a more restrictive aspect in an emergency. It gives the driver more time to stop. The main disadvantage of continuously-laid track equipment is its cost.

Intermittent track equipment is cheaper, but if it is provided only at signals (and speed restrictions) the computer is not updated until the next beacon, and the signal ahead may be in the driver's view for a considerable distance. If the driver has just passed a single-yellow signal when the signal ahead changes from red to a proceed aspect, the driver cannot accelerate, but must continue to brake as though the signal were still at red, because that is what the on-board computer still believes. Such slow running may not be acceptable in heavily worked areas, especially at junctions.

These delays can be reduced in two ways:

1. By providing additional 'fill-in' beacons between signals at critical locations, so that the computer can be updated sooner.
2. By allowing the driver to override the computer when he sees the signal ahead change from red, and speed has been reduced to a sufficiently low level, known as the release speed. This might appear to be less than entirely satisfactory from a safety point of view, but the release speed chosen is sufficiently low to enable the train to be stopped safely within the overlap of the signal at red should the driver attempt to go past it in error. If the train were to pass a red signal, an immediate brake application would result. The release speed is indicated on the speedometer by the illumination of a yellow LED.

If a driver is required to pass a red signal in an emergency, or because the signal has failed, he can override the ATP system by pressing a special button, but such action will only be effective if the train is stationary at the signal when the button is pressed. When a driver proceeds past a red signal in such a manner, his speed will be controlled to 20mph for 3min, unless he passes over another beacon within that time.

The BR-ATP system has now been accepted as a semi-permanent installation on the Great Western and Chiltern lines, and has also been installed on the Heathrow Express route and trains. Apart from possible infill, it is not intended to install the BR-ATP system elsewhere, and in due course it will be replaced by the pan-European ERTMS, which includes the ETCS pattern of ATP. However, the indications to the driver will not greatly differ from the ones he receives now.

21. The Train Protection and Warning System (TPWS)

TPWS has been developed as an enhancement of AWS to reduce the consequences of signals being wrongly passed at danger. It is not designed to prevent signals being passed at danger, but to mitigate the effect if such an event occurs. It is designed to cover the eventuality of a driver acknowledging the AWS warning at a caution signal and then failing to apply the brake. It also incorporates a train stop which will immediately apply the brake if a driver passes a signal at danger, a very valuable safeguard in the case of platform starting signals. TPWS will also be provided on the approach to buffer stops at passenger platforms, and on the approach to speed restrictions where approach speed is 60mph or more and the reduction in speed is at least one third.

TPWS is not intended to provide the same degree of protection as ATP, but it has the great benefit of being able to be installed in a much shorter time-scale. It is mandatory for it to be provided at all high-risk signals, ie those protecting crossovers or conflicting areas of movement. This will involve about 40% of the total number of signals, and experience has shown that these are the ones which are most likely to result in accidents.

Where TPWS is installed, the existing AWS will continue to operate normally.

Track Equipment
Track equipment consists of an overspeed sensor (known as a speed trap) on the approach to a signal, and a 'Train Stop' at a signal.

The Overspeed Sensor
The overspeed sensor initiates an emergency brake application if a train approaches a TPWS-equipped signal at danger at such a speed that the signal is likely to be passed. The precise location of the overspeed sensor and its speed setting depends on the gradient and certain

features regarding the track and signalling layout ahead, but is likely to be within the range 100 to 500yd before the signal. It will be remembered that there is normally a 200yd safety overlap beyond four-aspect colour light signals and it is intended that a train which has triggered the overspeed sensor will stop within the overlap except in the most serious cases of excessive speed when approaching a signal at danger. It is designed to be effective at approach speeds of up to 75mph for trains with good braking characteristics.

The sensor consists of an arming loop and a trigger loop. The arming loop causes a timer to be started in the TPWS equipment on the train, and if the trigger loop is reached before the timer has expired, a full AWS brake application will result.

The Train Stop
The train stop initiates an emergency brake application if the train passes a TPWS-equipped signal at danger. An override device is provided to inhibit the operation of the brake if the driver is authorised to pass the signal at danger.

The trainborne equipment consists of an aerial located underneath the traction unit, together with a TPWS Electronics Unit which replaces the existing AWS unit and includes the AWS functions.

TPWS Operation
When TPWS triggers an automatic brake application, the driver must ensure that the train comes to a stand, acknowledge the TPWS brake demand and report to the signaller at once. The driver must act in accordance with instructions given and make no further movement of the train until instructed to do so. The signaller must complete the appropriate form and report to Operations Control for instructions.

Note that isolation of the AWS will automatically isolate TPWS, but not vice versa.

A traction unit must not enter service if the TPWS is inoperative in any driving cab which is required to be used, unless the unit is to operate entirely over a non-TPWS route. If a defect arises in service, the instructions as shown for AWS will apply.

Options for Development
Protection for train speeds in excess of 75 mph can be obtained by providing additional overspeed sensors further back from the signal, or by adjusting the signalling controls to hold at Red the signal next in rear under certain conditions.

22. The European Rail Traffic Management System (ERTMS)

ERTMS and the European Train Control System resulted from a European Commission Council Directive 96/48/EC of 23 July 1996 concerning the inter-operability of the trans-European high-speed rail network. It was designed to provide a single standard train control system on that network to simplify through working from one country to another, and through a country, and to avoid all the complications which have arisen from the many different systems of signalling and train control in use at present in the countries of the European Union.

The term 'Train Control' is a rather comprehensive phrase dating back at least a century to the Great Western Railway's Automatic Train Control, so called because it could cause the brakes to be applied without any action on the part of the driver. BR-AWS deliberately avoided using the term 'Control' in case it should be interpreted as controlling the speed of the train, both upwards and downwards. It only initiated the braking action. The ATP element of ETCS also initiates the brake action, but train control includes the manner in which instructions are given to the driver, whether by lineside signals, cab signals or in any other manner. Train control, so far as ETCS is concerned, does not control the driving of the train; that remains with the driver. ETCS acts like ATP and intervenes only if the speed is too high in any given circumstance.

The term 'high-speed line' denotes one with speeds of 125mph and above, and in Britain will include the West Coast and East Coast main lines, the Great Western main line and the Channel Tunnel rail link. The Midland main line is likely to be included too. As a second stage it is likely that lower speed lines will fall within the ETCS requirements. Ultimately, ETCS will enable a train passing through many national administration areas to be equipped with ETCS only. By contrast, Eurostar at present requires no fewer than five separate sets of train control equipment.

A second advantage of a common ETCS system is that it will enable the European train control manufacturing industry to adopt a common specification, which should lead to a cheaper and more reliable product from various competing international manufacturers.

ETCS Variants

These are known as Levels 1, 2 and 3, Level 1 being the simplest and Level 3 the most advanced. Levels 2 and 3 use radio instead of cable as a means of communication. A radio project was started some years ago, known as the European Integrated Railways Radio Enhanced Network (EIRENE), to develop a radio system capable of carrying data for train control. This work resulted in the development of the Global System for Mobile Communication — Railways (GSM-R). The aims of the European Union and the European railways are to deliver a high-speed European-wide railway network equipped with ERTMS/ETCS and GSM-R. So far as Britain in Europe is concerned, the main benefit is likely to arise from speedier transits of freight across Europe to and from Britain, improving the competitive position of Britain's rail freight companies' *vis-à-vis* road transport.

ETCS Level 1

This is designed to be applied to a conventional line having lineside signals. Data is stored in balises (lineside or on-track transponders) linked to the signalling system and they pass information to the on-board computer. This enables the computer to calculate speed and braking curves for train protection purposes. The system provides continuous speed supervision and SPAD protection. Additional balises can be installed on the approach to signals to provide updated information.

ETCS Level 1 is the cheapest option and provides Automatic Train Protection only. Lineside signals and conventional train detection systems (track circuits and axle counters) continue to be used but it is possible to put the signal display in the cab. In practice, Level 1 is the ETCS version of BR-ATP, but as mentioned earlier, there are technical differences.

ETCS Level 2

Lineside signals are not necessary, as all the information that the driver needs is relayed to him by a secure radio system, known as GSM-R, and displayed on the driving cab console. Conventional train detection systems continue to be used.

Lineside signals may, however, be retained in certain circumstances: (1) to allow trains not equipped with ETCS to use the line concerned, (2) to provide a fall-back safeguard in case of failure of the radio control system.

It remains a fixed-block system and includes ATP.

ETCS Level 3

Lineside signals and conventional train detection systems are not used. The train's position is continuously calculated on board and transmitted to the Control Centre by secure radio links. Level 3 provides the option of 'moving block' in which trains can follow each other at less than braking distance apart, but this refinement is not likely to be available for some years. However, no work is currently being carried out on the development of level 3.

Trials are now taking place on several European railways using ETCS equipment at various levels. Trials are also taking place on the Cambrian lines.

23. Platform Starting Signals — Precautions

A number of accidents have occurred in the past when drivers have departed from a station and wrongly gone past the platform starting signal when it was at danger. Where there is a significant likelihood of such an event with a high probability of serious consequences, special safety precautions have been applied in recent years. These precautions are listed below, but it should be noted that a TPWS train stop will provide the most effective safeguard in the future.

The likelihood of a signal being passed at danger is considered to exist where it controls the exit from a platform which is served by:

1. Regular suburban services with frequent stops and repetitive work, or
2. Other types of service where the signal concerned has a history of being wrongly passed at danger.

The probability of serious consequences from the signal being wrongly passed at danger is assessed by the type of conflicting movement which could occur, the likely outcome of a collision and the density of traffic.

Method of Assessment

All platform starting signals protecting pointwork which forms part of a running junction have been assessed according to the degree of risk, on a points basis. The number of trains starting from the platform concerned in the busiest 12 hours (normally 07.00 to 19.00 on a weekday) is multiplied by the number of trains where, if the platform starting signal is wrongly passed at danger, a head-on collision could take place, a converging collision could result or a collision could occur with another train crossing its path. The points allocated to each type of collision are suitably weighted, based on the severity of the possible consequences.

Special Safety Precautions

At those signals where the number of points is over a certain figure, ie at the higher end of the risk scale, special precautions are provided. These may be:

• All trains booked to call at the platform must be provided with Automatic Train Protection or equivalent, or
• trap points with a sand drag must be provided ahead of the signal, or
• the interlocking must prevent any conflicting route being set up for another train when a route is set up to the platform starting signal or when a train is standing at that signal, or
• the track layout must be changed to avoid the problem.

A suitable precaution must be applied for all new works and rationalisation schemes. At other places these precautions may be applied retrospectively, or one of the following must be provided:

• A detonator (or modern electronic equivalent) immediately beyond the platform starting signal, with a visual warning device (a SPAD indicator) 50yd beyond that signal.
• An additional AWS permanent magnet immediately beyond the platform starting signal and, where appropriate, beyond one or more of any intermediate train stop markers in the platform.

This is a description of the current procedures, but a new system of risk assessment is to be applied to all junction signals by October 2005 which will require overrun risk to be considered at the design stage and designed out if possible (eg by flank protection).

Driver's Reminder Appliance (DRA)

Drivers have long been aware of the possibility of inadvertently starting away against platform starting signals at danger, caused in part by the receipt of the 'Ready to start' bell signal from the guard, and some drivers have had their own method of reminding themselves that the platform starting signal is at danger. This has now been regularised by the provision in most passenger train driving cabs of a reminder appliance in the form of a large button which the driver must depress when stopped at any signal at danger. When depressed, the button illuminates red and prevents traction power being applied until the button is pulled out. The driver must not reset the DRA until the signal clears.

Additionally, the driver must set the DRA when he stops at a platform where there is no starting signal, in any of the following circumstances:

• When he has just passed a caution signal.
• When he has been authorised to pass a signal at danger.
• When he has entered the platform under the authority of a position light signal or a subsidiary signal.

He must not reset the DRA until the 'Ready to start' signal is received.

Some new trains are fitted with an 'active' DRA which is applied automatically when a train passes a caution signal.

As an additional safety measure, the guard must check (where practicable) that the platform starting signal has been cleared before he gives the 'Ready to start' signal to the driver. The same arrangement applies to a person in charge of a platform before he gives a handsignal to the guard to indicate that station work is complete or gives the 'Ready to start' signal to the driver of a driver-only train.

Where a rightaway indicator, displaying the letters 'RA' when operated, is provided, the indication will not be displayed until the platform starting signal is cleared.

24. Signals Passed at Danger Without Authority (SPADs)

During the 1990s there was growing concern about the number of instances of signals being passed at danger. This was given emphasis by the Southall and Ladbroke Grove collisions in 1997 and 1999 respectively, and from an increase, albeit slight, in the number of SPADs in 1998/9. Several initiatives have therefore been taken to improve the position, and it is particularly important to cover the short period before TPWS becomes effective at critical signals system-wide by the end of 2003.

Most of the initiatives are organisational, but a number of steps are being taken to give drivers prior warning that they are approaching a signal which does not have a good approach view and which may come upon them quite suddenly. Countdown markers of the type used approaching motorway exits have been provided in a number of cases.

SPAD Indicators

At certain locations where there is a particularly high risk of collision if a signal is passed at danger, SPAD indicators have been erected. They are similar to a normal three-aspect colour light signal but have a blue backboard and are located about 50yd beyond the signal concerned. (See page 92.)

SPAD indicators normally display no aspect, but when the signal to which they refer is passed at danger they immediately display the following aspects to tell the driver that he has passed a signal at danger — the top and bottom aspects flash red and the centre aspect displays a steady red light. The driver must stop at once and tell the signaller what has happened. The driver must also stop his train and report to the signaller if he sees a SPAD indicator flashing for a signal on another line. This is a safety precaution in case his train is on a collision course with the other train.

A SPAD indicator may also have an AWS magnet positioned on its approach. It is suppressed for normal signalled movements, but will give an AWS warning when the SPAD indicator is triggered.

Signal Sighting

Signal sighting is a very important factor when determining the precise location of new signals, and it is equally important when changes in the environment of signals may impede the driver's view of signals. Such changes may result from, for example, building work, the growth of lineside vegetation and the installation of overhead electrification.

Signal sighting refers to the driver's approach view of signals, including the time during which the signal is in view. The location of signals is paramount. Signals must therefore be positioned in order to give the best possible sighting for the driver.

Signal Sighting Committee

Signal Sighting Committees exist to determine exactly where new signals should be sited, and whether any changes should be made to existing signals whose sighting is in question for any reason, eg after a SPAD at a signal which has had previous SPADs or where a driver reports that sighting is unsatisfactory. A committee consists of a chairman and a number of people who are competent in engineering and train driver requirements, including a competent representative of a train operating company operating over the route.

Sighting considerations are paramount, and the following factors must be borne in mind:

- The type of signal and the method of displaying the signal head, eg straight post, angled post, gantry, etc.
- Provision of the minimum sighting time, viz 7sec approach view and 4sec uninterrupted view. These times are currently being reconsidered.
- The red aspect should be as near as possible to the driver's eye level.
- The centre of the light beam should be aligned towards a point 10ft above the left-hand running rail at 200yd from the signal.
- The desirability of providing banner or co-acting signals.

Other factors to be considered are:

- Where practicable, avoid sites on viaducts, steep gradients, in tunnels, across level crossings, part-train length beyond a platform.
- Have regard to the position of neutral sections on overhead electrified lines and conductor rail gaps on third rail electrified lines to avoid the risk of trains being brought to a stand on 'dead' sections.
- The avoidance of environmental nuisance to lineside neighbours near signals at which trains are regularly stopped, consisting of braking and acceleration noises and the sounds of engines idling and compressors working.
- The possibility of vandalism to trains or signalling equipment.
- The possibility of pilferage from stationary freight trains.

There should be regular inspections of existing signals both by day and by night. It should be noted that ETCS Levels 2 and 3 avoid the problem by, in effect, putting the signals in the driving cab.

The Signaller's Actions

If a train passes a signal at danger without authority, the signaller must immediately arrange for the train to be stopped, eg by speaking to the driver by radio, and take any other emergency action. He must ask the driver a number of questions printed on a SPAD report form. Details must be given to Operations Control and the signaller must not allow the train to proceed without the Control's authority. If there is any doubt about the correct working of a signal it must be treated as being defective.

SPAD alarms are being provided in Integrated Electronic Control Centres to alert the signalman and give an immediate audible alarm and visual message when a signal is passed at danger. The visual message displays the identification numbers of the signal and train concerned

The Electric Token Block System

In many respects the principles of the Absolute Block double line system apply to the working of single lines, but in addition to the normal dangers of working trains over a double line there is the extra hazard on single lines of a head-on collision caused by a train irregularly entering a section already occupied by a train coming the other way. To safeguard against this, the Electric Token Block system was devised, based on the principle that every train passing through a single line section must carry a token, obtained from a token instrument, of which there is one at each end of each section. The instruments at each end of a section are electrically interlocked so that it is possible for only one token to be 'out' (ie in use) for the section at one and the same time. The token may take the form of a circular tablet, a few inches in diameter, or a metal key about 6in long. It is placed in a leather pouch with a large loop handle to facilitate the handover from signaller to driver, and vice versa. The token is withdrawn from the token instrument when the 'Is line clear' bell signal is acknowledged, and is inserted in the instrument at the other end of the section when the train has passed through the section and the 'Train out of section' bell signal is sent. Each instrument contains several tokens.

At a crossing loop on a single line, a train may be accepted only from the signalbox in rear if the loop line for which the facing points are set and on which the train will run is clear to the loop exit signal. When trains are approaching a crossing place from opposite directions, the home signals in both directions must be kept at danger, until the train which is to enter the loop first has stopped, after which the home signal may be cleared to allow it to draw forward. When it has stopped again in the loop the home signal may be cleared for the other train to enter the loop.

The Tokenless Block System

In this system, safety is provided for by the sequential occupation and clearance of track circuits at both signalboxes, so that the signals cannot be cleared for a second train to enter the section from either direction until the previous train is proved to have passed through the section. Tokens are not used, hence the name of the system.

The method of signalling is as follows:

Trains are accepted by placing the 'Acceptance' switch in the 'Accept' position. This is the usual position, depending on the anticipated movement of trains.

Left: **Tyer's single line tablet instrument.**
J. H. Edser

Right: Typical single track branch line with passing loops worked under the electronic block system.

Lower right: Sequence of indicators and boards at a crossing loop on a single track line worked under the electronic token block system.

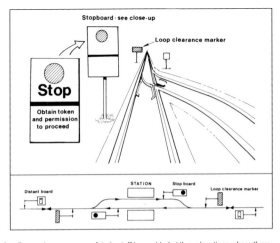

Before the dispatch of a train, the signaller must press the 'Offer' button, provided that the block indicator and the acceptance switch for that section are normal. If the acceptance switch at the signalbox in advance is at 'Accept', the block indicators in both signalboxes will move to 'Train accepted', and the signaller in rear may then clear his signal and tell his colleague the description of the train. When the train occupies the track circuit ahead of the section signal, the block indicator will move to 'Train in section'. After the train has passed through the section, it registers its arrival by operating a treadle at the home signal; and after it has occupied and cleared the track circuit ahead of the home signal the signaller there must place the acceptance switch to normal. When the train, complete with tail lamp, arrives, the signaller must operate the 'Train arrived' button, which will restore the block indicators to 'Normal'. The acceptance switch must be maintained at normal until the train has passed the clearing point.

One-train Working

This system is in widespread use on dead-end branch lines where the train service is so infrequent that it does not require more than one train to be on the branch at once. There are two methods — in one a token known as a train staff is provided and the driver must not enter the branch line unless he is in possession of it. In the other method there is no train staff, and the clearance of the controlling signal is the only authority for the train to enter the branch. Safety in the latter case is achieved by the occupation and clearance of a track circuit, located at the entrance to the branch, on two occasions (ie when the train enters and when it returns). The controlling signal cannot be cleared for a second train until the first one is proved to have returned by the operation of the track circuits.

A train staff is provided at those locations where there is someone, usually a signaller, who can act as its custodian and hand it over to the driver when required. The other method is used mainly on lines controlled from a remote signalbox, such as a power signalbox, where there is no one available at or near the branch entrance who can look after the train staff.

The 'No Signaller' Token System

This is a system in use mainly on dead-end branch lines which allows one train to follow another one along a branch line as soon as the first train is proved to have arrived at the far end of the branch. It is achieved by the use of tokens, and a token instrument at each end of the branch line. The token instrument at the junction of the main line and the branch is operated by the signaller and he issues a token in the usual way to a driver to proceed on to the branch line, provided that no other token is 'out'. When the train arrives at the far end of the branch, and is clear of an 'End of Single Line Section' notice board, the driver places the token in an instrument there, thus allowing another train to use the branch line, either by following him or by setting off in the opposite direction. It avoids the cost of having a signalbox and signaller at the branch end. The signaller controls the issue of tokens from the machine at the far end, by the use of a release.

Failures of Equipment

With all these systems, provision must be made for train movements to continue safely, albeit at reduced speed, when the signalling equipment controlling the tokens is faulty, or a token is lost or damaged, or track circuits have failed. It is vital to ensure that only one train at a time is in the single line section, and this is done by introducing a system known as 'Working by Pilotman'. In this system someone is appointed Pilotman, who is responsible for

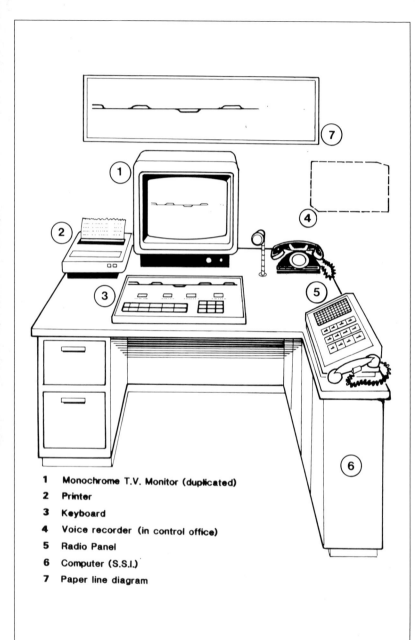

1 Monochrome T.V. Monitor (duplicated)
2 Printer
3 Keyboard
4 Voice recorder (in control office)
5 Radio Panel
6 Computer (S.S.I.)
7 Paper line diagram

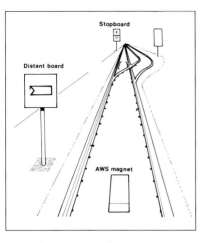

Above: Sequence of indicators and boards at a crossing loop on a single track line worked under the Radio Electronic Token Block system (RETB).

Left: Signalman's RETB console.

Right: RETB Stop Board, instructing the driver to stop and obtain permission to proceed. Underneath is the Radio Area Code Change sign. *D. C. Hall*

the safety of the single line. He must personally authorise drivers to proceed, and travel through with the driver when the next train requiring to pass through the single line section will do so from the other end. On 'One-train Working' sections the Pilotman must travel with every train.

The Radio Electronic Token Block (RETB) System

This system was born out of the need to reduce the costs of working the long single lines to be found in northern Scotland, central Wales and elsewhere, in order to avoid having to close them down. It requires no intermediate signalboxes or signallers, nor does it require a vulnerable telegraph pole route, because all messages are sent by radio. It is based in theory on the well-tried and reliable Electric Token Block system but the 'token' is passed between signaller and driver electronically by radio, instead of physically by hand.

The whole line is controlled by one signaller, who has at his disposal an operating console containing a representation of the track under his control, together with electronic equipment and computers which look after safety. Each locomotive is equipped with radio and an

RETB instrument with two windows in which the electronic token displays its presence by showing the two ends of the section through which the driver is authorised to travel.

When the driver wishes to enter a single line section he radios the signaller for permission. If the previous train in the same direction has passed through the section and cleared the next crossing loop, and if no train has been authorised to proceed through the section from the other end, the signaller will issue an electronic token to the driver. To enable this to take place, both the driver and the signaller must press a button on their equipment simultaneously (known as a 'handshake'). The driver will then confirm that he has received the token, because it will have appeared on the RETB instrument in his cab, and the signaller will verbally authorise him to proceed (this takes the place of the section signal). On entering

the single line section the driver will report to the signaller by radio as soon as his train has cleared the loop. This is important for two reasons — as soon as the loop is clear another train travelling in the same direction can be allowed to leave the loop in rear, and secondly, if for any reason the driver had left the loop and entered the single line section without authority (potentially very dangerous) the signaller would become aware of it and tell the driver

Above: **Hydro-pneumatic points on an RETB line.** *D. C. Hall*

to stop at once. He would also issue a similar instruction to the driver of any train coming through the single line section in the opposite direction.

In order to keep costs down, the points at loops are not normally worked by the signaller (who is likely to be many miles away) but are hydro-pneumatically operated so that they always lie towards the same loop line. They are capable of being trailed through from the other loop line. A points-indicator may be provided for the facing direction, which exhibits a steady yellow light when the points are fitting correctly.

When a train has entered a loop and is clear of the single line section, the driver will inform the signaller accordingly by radio. Both men will press the appropriate buttons on their equipment simultaneously and the electronic token will be returned to the signaller. The driver's RETB instrument display will clear and the token will appear on the signaller's console display. If the section ahead is clear, the procedure for the issue of an electronic token for that section may then take place to enable the driver to proceed.

The signalbox computer ensures that tokens are issued in the correct sequence, keeps a record of all trains on the line and prevents the signaller from authorising conflicting train movements.

The RETB system can be modified in several ways. The loop points can be operated, detected and locked by radio command to avoid the train having to pass through them at low speed. Transponders located in the track can detect the position of the train and announce it by radio to the signaller.

PART 6

26. Level Crossings —
Manually Operated with Gates or Barriers

Manually-operated level crossings are of the following types (the total number in use in 2000 is also shown):

- Gates operated by a signaller or crossing keeper on site   268
- Barriers operated by a signaller or crossing keeper on site   274
- Barriers operated remotely by a signaller or crossing keeper and supervised by CCTV   338

It should be noted that level crossing gates and barriers are not considered to be an obstruction so far as the acceptance of trains is concerned.

Gates Operated by a Signaller on Site
The gates swing alternately across the road and the railway, but legally are required normally to be closed across the road. However, HM Railway Inspectorate may authorise the gates at any particular level crossing to be normally closed across the railway, and this has been done at most level crossings because of the frequency of road traffic. The gates are interlocked with the railway signals in such a way that the signals cannot be cleared unless the gates are across the road. Once the signals have been cleared, the gates cannot then be moved back across the railway. Where necessary, wicket gates may be provided, normally capable of being locked in the closed position by the signaller.

Where road traffic is heavy, and the signaller finds it difficult to swing his gates across the road because there are insufficient gaps in the traffic, road traffic light signals may be provided, which the signaller can switch to red to enable him to swing his gates. The gates are often operated by a large wheel in the signalbox, but in other cases are pushed across by hand.

Gates Operated by a Crossing Keeper on Site
These installations are usually to be found in rural areas where neither road nor rail traffic is heavy. For historical reasons they are of many types. They may be operated by a crossing keeper who lives in a cottage at the crossing, or they may be operated by non-resident crossing keepers working shifts, or by a combination of both, depending on the flow of road and rail traffic.

The gates may be of the signalbox type alternately closing the road and the railway, or they may be field gates, which open away from the railway. The gates are normally pushed across by hand.

Protecting railway signals are provided at some, but not all, of this type of crossing. In some cases both distant and stop signals are provided (normally semaphore); in other cases only distant signals are provided. Sometimes the signals are interlocked with the gates, and sometimes they are not.

There are various methods of informing the crossing keeper as to whether he may open the gates to allow road traffic to cross. At some crossings duplicate block indicators are provided. Duplicate bells may be provided. At other crossings the crossing keeper has to telephone a nearby signalbox to ask the signaller if road traffic may be allowed across.

Barriers Operated by a Signaller or Crossing Keeper on Site (Known as Manually Controlled Barrier Crossings, or MCB
Lifting barriers are normally installed as a modern replacement for gates, and are operated electrically. The barriers extend across the full width of the road at each side of the level crossing when lowered, but are normally kept in the raised position. They are interlocked with the protecting railway signals and there are usually road traffic light signals too.

Right: Control console for the lifting barriers at Oakham MCB level crossing.
D. C. Hall

When the operator wishes to lower the barriers he will press a button marked 'Lower' on his control console. The amber light on the road traffic signals will show for about three seconds, after which the red lights will start to flash. Between four and eight seconds later the nearside barriers will start to descend, and when they are fully lowered, the offside barriers will descend. The operator must then check that the crossing is clear (ie that no vehicle or person is trapped on the crossing between the lowered barriers) and press a 'Crossing Clear' button, before he can clear his railway signals. Both the barrier lowering and raising sequences can be initiated automatically by trains through the operation of track circuits, but it will still be necessary for the operator to check that the crossing is clear, and press the 'Crossing Clear' button before he can clear his railway signals. After the train has passed, all the barriers rise simultaneously.

There is a category of level crossing known as a Remote Control Level Crossing which is not adjacent to the signalbox but is not more than 300yd away and can be observed clearly from the signalbox without the need for CCTV.

Barriers Operated Remotely by a Signaller or Crossing Keeper and Supervised by CCTV
The barrier equipment and method of control are similar to an MCB crossing, the only difference being that instead of the signaller checking visually that the crossing is clear he does so by means of a closed circuit television

camera mounted at the level crossing, which relays a picture to a screen in the signalbox. Audible and visual indications are provided at the signalbox to show if the main power supply fails, or if a barrier is dislodged (eg by high wind, or a road vehicle running into it).

CCTV installations enable a signaller to control level crossings away from the signalbox, and allow crossing keepers to control additional distant level crossings. One operator can control several crossings, and CCTV operation is widely used in power signalbox areas. CCTV crossings are always interlocked with signals.

27. Automatic Level Crossings

The following types of automatic level crossings existing in 2000 (with totals) are:

• Automatic half-barrier crossings (AHB)   465
• Automatic barrier crossings, locally monitored   43
  (ABCL)
• Automatic open crossings, locally monitored   140
  (AOCL)

Below: **An automatic half-barrier level crossing, showing the layout, road traffic signals with twin flashing red lights (1) and single amber light (2), barriers (3), signs, telephone to signalbox (4), etc.**

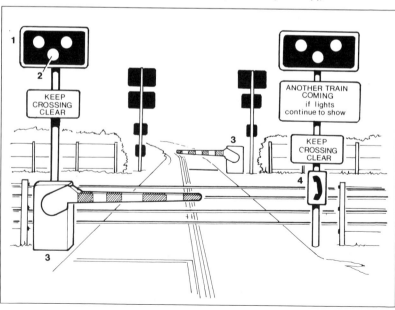

Right: Road users' advance warning of an AHB crossing. 1. Automatic barriers stop when lights show. 2. Drivers of large or slow vehicles must phone before crossing to get permission to cross. 3. Drivers of large or slow vehicles must park here and use phone at crossing.

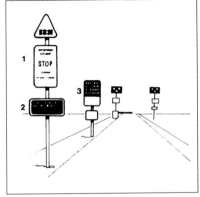

(ABCL crossings are a quite recent development, hence the small number.)

Automatic Half-barrier Crossings (Known as AHB Crossings)

These were first introduced on BR in 1961, and they have three objectives:

1. To avoid the manning costs of ordinary level crossings.
2. To reduce the delays to road traffic which conventional gated or manned barrier level crossings cause.
3. To improve safety at level crossings, by eliminating the human element.

So far as these three objectives are concerned, AHBs are introduced only where their costs are more than outweighed by the saving in staff costs. They considerably reduce delays to road traffic because they are not interlocked with railway signals, therefore the crossing does not need to be closed for such a long period. At a manned crossing the road has to be closed and the railway signals cleared before the driver of an approaching train has come within sight of the distant signal. At AHBs the railway signals act independently of the operation of the level crossing — the nearest railway signals may be green whilst road traffic is passing over the crossing. So far as safety is concerned, they only eliminate the railway human element. They do not eliminate the careless or reckless motorist who ignores the red flashing lights and deliberately zigzags round the barriers, occasionally at the cost of his life.

The barriers are operated by an approaching train occupying a particular track circuit, reinforced by a treadle at the running-on end to guard against unreliable operation of the track circuit by lightweight vehicles, which triggers the following sequence of events:

1. An amber light shows for about 3sec.
2. Twin red lights commence to flash alternately.
3. Between 4 and 6sec later the barriers start to lower. The barrier lowering operation takes 6-10sec.
4. A warning sounds during the whole of this period.
5. Not less than 27sec after the amber lights first show, the train passes over the crossing.
6. The barriers rise as soon as the train has cleared the crossing but, if another train is approaching the barriers, will remain down unless at least 10sec can

Above: Speed restriction board for trains approaching an AHB level crossing in the wrong direction.

elapse after the barriers have begun to rise, before the operating cycle recommences for the other train.

The equipment at the crossing is monitored from a control point (usually a signalbox) and telephones are provided for the public to speak to the control point.

AHBs may be provided only where the following conditions apply:

1. The maximum speed of trains must not exceed 100mph.
2. There must not be more than two running lines (though there may be two sidings as well).
3. The road on the approaches to the crossing must be wide enough to enable vehicles to pass safely (ie without blocking back on to the crossing whilst waiting to pass).

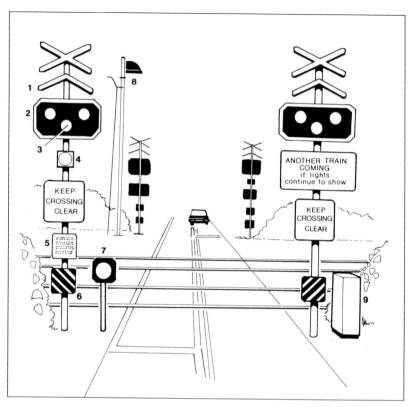

Above: An automatic open crossing locally monitored, showing the layout, road traffic signals, signs etc. 1. Crossing sign denoting two tracks; 2. Twin flashing red lights; 3. Single amber light; 4. Yodalarm unit; 5. Sign showing local Railtrack telephone numbers; 6. Telephone; 7. Red flashing signal 'another train coming'; 8. Floodlight angled to crossing; 9. Local control unit.

---

4. There must be no bumps or hollows on the road that might cause a low vehicle to ground on the crossing (known as the vertical profile).

5. The road layout (ie nearby junctions) and traffic conditions (ie frequent hold-ups) must be such that there is no significant risk of road vehicles blocking back and obstructing the railway.

Equipment is provided at the level crossing to allow the

lights and barriers to be operated on site, and this occurs in a number of circumstances, such as:

1. Failure of equipment.
2. Repairs to equipment.
3. Work on the track.
4. Road works near the crossing which might cause traffic to block back.

When the crossing is being controlled locally, the signaller must warn the driver of each train to approach the crossing cautiously and not pass over it unless authorised by a green flag or lamp being displayed by the attendant.

Some AHB crossings are adapted to allow wrong direction movements to operate the barrier equipment in the normal way. They are known as AHB-X level crossings, but speed must not exceed that shown on the wrong direction speed restriction board (black numerals prefixed by the letter X on a white background), normally positioned on the right-hand side of the line.

When barriers fail in the lowered position, or the red

road traffic signals continue to flash during a failure of equipment at an automatic open crossing, no railwayman may authorise road users to disregard the road traffic signals. Only a policeman in uniform may do this. The policeman will contact the signaller by using the level crossing telephone and may not be given authority to allow road traffic to cross until protecting signals have been placed to danger. After this has been done, trains may not be allowed to approach the crossing until the policeman has given an assurance that road traffic has been stopped.

Automatic Barrier Crossings Locally Monitored (ABCL) and Automatic Open Crossings Locally Monitored (AOCL)

These types of equipment are installed where the nature of the train service allows speeds to be reduced on the approach to the crossing to a level at which the train driver can check (1) that the road traffic signals are flashing (and the barriers at ABCLs are lowered) and (2) that the crossing is not obstructed by a stationary or very slow moving road vehicle; and that the train can stop before reaching the crossing in the event of failure or obstruction. ABCLs and AOCLs are cheaper to install than AHBs because the monitoring of operation is done locally by the train driver, instead of remotely (using expensive cable) by the signaller. Also, the road requirements at AOCLs are not so stringent as they are at AHB crossings. There are many level crossings on secondary lines, especially those operated on only two shifts, where an AHB crossing would be too expensive, but where an economic case can be made for the installation of locally monitored level crossing equipment.

There are certain restrictions upon the provision of AOCL crossings, depending upon the 'traffic moment' (a measure of the combined volume of road and rail traffic) whereas the ABCL crossing has no such restrictions, but the ABCL crossing must satisfy some additional road conditions.

The road traffic signals (and the half-barriers at ABCLs) are operated automatically by the occupation of track circuits by approaching trains, but in addition, treadles are provided at the strike-in point owing to problems with the unreliability of track circuit operation by lightweight vehicles. A white flashing light, adjacent to the crossing and facing the train driver, indicates that the road traffic signals are operating correctly. A red light flashes when the white light is not flashing, and when this happens the driver must stop short of the crossing.

The train driver is warned that he is approaching a locally monitored crossing by a board bearing a black St George's cross on a white background. He must then reduce his speed (if necessary) so that he can pass a speed restriction board at the appropriate speed. On passing the speed restriction board (black numerals and a black St Andrew's cross on a white background) he must check that the crossing is clear and that the white

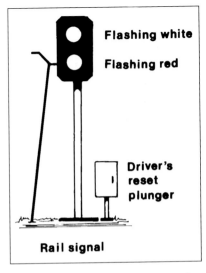

Above: **Signal for train driver on approach to automatic open crossing.**

light is flashing, then proceed to the crossing at the speed shown on the speed restriction board, known as the crossing speed. The maximum crossing speed allowed is 55mph.

If the white light adjacent to the crossing is not flashing, or if the crossing cannot be seen to be clear, or in other specified circumstances, the driver must stop short of the crossing and not proceed over it until he is sure it is safe to do so. The horn must be sounded continuously until the front of the train is on the crossing. However, a train must not pass over an AOCL crossing during darkness or poor visibility when the road traffic signals have failed unless it is a passenger or ECS train with the lights on, or other safety arrangements have been made.

The speed restriction board is located near the point at which the operating cycle for the crossing commences. The operating cycle is as follows:

1. An amber light shows for 3sec.
2. The twin red road traffic signals start to flash alternately.
3. The train arrives at the crossing not less than 27sec after the amber light first shows.

The crossing speed is therefore determined by the speed necessary to give 27sec warning from the point at which the crossing comes into the driver's view. The crossing

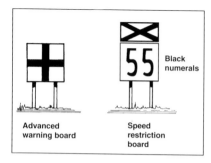

Advanced warning board

Speed restriction board

Black numerals

Above: **Lineside signs warning the train driver that he is approaching an AOCL:
1. Warning board; 2. Speed restriction board.**

Above: **Miniature warning lights and notice boards at a level crossing.** *Author*

speed board must not be more than 600m (approx 660yd) from the flashing rail signals at the crossing.

Some speed restriction boards carry two figures. The bottom figure (which is the higher speed) applies to passenger trains and to parcels and postal trains composed entirely of bogie vehicles and to light engines. The top figure (the lower speed) applies to all other trains.

Level crossings are often situated at or near the ends of station platforms. In such cases a speed restriction board is not provided, but there is a STOP board near the crossing. When the train is ready to restart, a plunger is pressed, which causes the road traffic signals to flash. The driver must check before starting and passing the STOP board that the crossing is clear and that the white light is flashing. He must then sound the horn. At some places the flashing of the lights is caused automatically, instead of manually by plunger.

An audible warning is sounded at the crossing as a train approaches, and if the lights continue to flash after the train has passed over the crossing, the audible warning will change and a special flashing light will indicate the words 'Another train coming'. There are no telephones but a plate gives the telephone number of a suitable railway office and also the name of the crossing.

Equipment is provided at some crossings to enable wrong direction movements to be made in the normal way, similar to the arrangements at AHB-X crossings. These crossings are known as ABCL-X and AOCL-X crossings.

28. Other Level Crossings

Open Crossings

Open level crossings are to be found on quiet single lines, where the traffic moment is not more than 30 in any hour. Traffic moment denotes the combination of trains and road vehicles, eg 15 road vehicles and two trains an hour

would represent a traffic moment of 30. The crossings are non-automatic, there are no gates or barriers, and there are no flashing red road traffic signals. Road signs require road users to give way to trains, and satisfactory visibility of approaching trains is necessary. Trains either approach the crossing at 10mph, or stop at a Stop Board 25yd from it. They must stop if the road users' view of approaching trains is inadequate (or vice versa). There are no telephones.

On the railway, an Advance Warning Board is provided at braking distance to enable trains to reduce speed to 10mph, or stop. The board carries a black St George's cross on a white background. A speed restriction/whistle board is provided at a point from which the driver has a clear view of the crossing and from which he can stop the train short of the crossing if necessary.

There were 60 of these crossings in 2000.

Level Crossings with Gates or Barriers Operated by the Road User or a Member of the Traincrew
These fall into three categories:

• Crossings equipped with miniature warning lights 135
• Crossings equipped with a telephone 1,381
• Crossings with no equipment 2,507

Almost all the level crossings we have considered in previous chapters have been on public roads, but the great majority of those which will be dealt with in this chapter are private, and the public have no right to use them with a road vehicle, although there are footpath or bridleway rights at some. Private crossings are of two types:

Occupation Level Crossings

These concern private roads which existed before the railway was built. The road may have served only one farm, or it may have served several farms and/or cottages. When the railway was built, the tracks were laid across the private road, creating an occupation crossing. In addition to those who have a right to use the crossing by virtue of residence, others who have business there may also use the crossing, eg the postman, the baker and other tradesmen.

Accommodation Level Crossings

When the railway line was built it often ran through a piece of land in one ownership, dividing it into two. In order to provide access from one part of the divided land to the other it was necessary to construct accommodation bridges and level crossings, which frequently merely give access from a field at one side of the railway to another field at the other side. Many of these crossings, of which there are several thousand, have fallen into disuse over the years, but still exist legally.

The gates at occupation and accommodation crossings are almost always of the field type, which open away from the railway and normally bear a notice requiring the user to shut and fasten the gates after use, with a penalty for failure to do so.

Crossings Equipped with Miniature Warning Lights

These crossings have small red and green lights, operated by approaching trains, for the guidance of road users, and detailed instructions as to the use of the crossing are displayed on notice boards at the crossing. The green light shows continuously until a train running at maximum line speed is about 40sec away, when it will be extinguished and the red light will show. If no light shows, the notice board warns the user to beware, or to telephone the signaller if a telephone is provided. A telephone to a signalbox may be provided if, for example, heavy farm plant or herds of cattle are regularly taken over the crossing or if the crossing is a public one.

Crossings Where a Telephone is Provided

At private level crossings the road user is responsible for his own safety and must satisfy himself that it is safe to cross before doing so. Where the sighting distance of trains from the crossing is inadequate, or herds of animals or heavy machinery are taken over, a telephone to a signalbox may be provided so that the user can ask

Above: **Instruction board at an occupation level crossing equipped with a telephone.** *D. C. Hall*

the signaller if the crossing may be used. The signaller must find out what is to be taken over the crossing and if there is sufficient time for that movement to take place before the next train, the user must be so informed. If there is insufficient time, he must tell the user to wait and telephone again. All calls are recorded by the signaller.

The gates at private level crossings need not be locked.

It should be noted that there are a few public level crossings which, for historical reasons, do not conform to the principles set out in Part 6.

Hot axlebox detectors are provided on main lines about every 20/25 miles, especially where there are no lineside signalboxes. Signallers in lineside signalboxes are expected to look out for signs of hot axleboxes on passing trains, and have the trains stopped if necessary. Signallers can recognise a hot axlebox in a number of ways — by the smell of overheated material, by the sight of smoke or flames and by the screeching noise made by dry, hot axleboxes.

In the absence of a lineside signaller, hot axleboxes are detected by equipment located on the track. The hot axlebox detector (HABD for short) scans the axlebox passing over it for infra-red radiation which is emitted at normal and hot axle bearing temperatures. An alarm is sounded in the monitoring signalbox if a hot axle bearing is detected.

If the alarm sounds in the signalbox, the signaller will put the signals to danger to stop the train. He will also stop trains on adjoining lines until the train with the hot axlebox has stopped and the driver has assured him that no other lines are affected (by a derailed vehicle, for example). As soon as the signaller has placed the signals to danger, he must contact Operations Control to see whether the vehicle concerned is conveying dangerous goods.

When the driver reports to the signaller (normally by telephone), the signaller must tell him the axle number counting from the front of the train (including the locomotive) and whether left-hand or right-hand side (the signalbox equipment displays these details). The driver must then examine the axlebox concerned for evidence of overheating, if necessary by feeling it or using a device known as a 'tempilstik', and report his findings to the signaller.

If the axlebox is obviously hot, but the vehicle concerned is safe to be moved, it must be detached in a nominated siding (speed not to exceed 10mph on plain line and 5mph over points and crossings). If it is a passenger coach, the passengers should be moved out of the vehicle before detaching takes place. The signaller must stop trains on adjoining lines before authorising the driver to make the movement.

If the axle concerned is fitted with roller bearings and no defect can be found, the train may proceed normally, but a further examination must be carried out within 50 miles by either a rolling stock technician or the driver, unless the train passes over a hot axlebox detector in working order without activating the alarm. If further examination reveals that there is nothing wrong, the train may resume its normal journey. If, however, the second detector sounds an alarm and the train has to be moved, speed must not exceed 20mph.

If the axle concerned is not fitted with roller bearings and no evidence of overheating can be found, the driver

Left: **A hot axlebox detector.** *Author*

must report the circumstances to the signaller at once and act in accordance with instructions given. If the train has to be moved, it must not exceed 20mph.

These instructions do not apply to steam locomotives in steam which, by their very nature, are prone to cause false alarms.

The instructions to drivers and signallers contained in the Rule Book, Sec H (ii) are lengthy and complex, covering no fewer than 10 pages. The description in this chapter is merely a summary.

Additional features may be added, such as hot wheel detection caused by binding brakes and wheel impact detection caused by wheel flats.

30. Permanent Speed Restrictions

All Railtrack's running lines are engineered and maintained for trains to run at specific speeds, and these are published to the staff concerned as maximum permitted speeds for the route concerned. These speeds, known as line speeds, are not constant throughout the route, but vary over different sections. The maximum permitted speed is indicated by signs at the lineside, which are either yellow cut-out numerals, or reflectorised circular signs with black numerals and a red border.

At certain places on the route, speed has to be reduced below the normal line speed owing, for example, to sharp curvature or complexity of track layout. These reductions of speed are known as permanent speed restrictions (PSR for short).

In order to assist the driver when he is approaching a location at which he needs to reduce speed (which may be either a section with a lower line speed, or a permanent speed restriction), an advance warning sign, known as a warning indicator, may be provided, sufficiently far back to allow the driver time to reduce speed to the required level. The warning indicator takes the form of a reflectorised triangular sign with black numerals and a yellow border. In addition, an AWS permanent magnet may be provided on the approach side of the sign, so that an audible warning is given in the driving cab. The brakes are applied automatically if the driver does not acknowledge the warning.

Warning indicators are provided where the approach speed is 60mph or more and the reduction of speed is approximately one-third or more from the approach speed, eg:

Approach speed	Speed reduced to, or below
125mph	85mph
100mph	65mph
80mph	50mph
60mph	35mph

The approach speed is considered to be the maximum permitted speed on the immediate approach to the

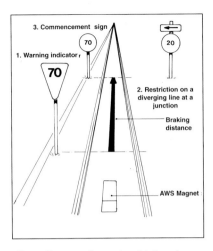

Above: **Permanent speed restriction signs: 1. Warning indicator; 2. Sign for speed restriction on a diverging route at a junction.; 3. Commencement of speed restriction.**

restriction, but a lower speed may be assumed in certain circumstances.

Where there is a 'cascade' of speed restrictions (two or more within 2 miles), none of which may individually justify a warning indicator, but where there is a total speed reduction of more than one-third between the approach speed to the first restriction and the last in the cascade, a warning indicator shall be provided for the PSR in the series which takes the total reduction in speed to more than one-third.

Where the warning indicator applies to a diverging line it will carry an arrow, pointing left or right as appropriate. Where differential speeds apply, the warning indicator will show two speeds, one above the other. The bottom figure, showing the higher speed, applies only to passenger (loaded or empty), postal and parcels trains composed entirely of bogie vehicles, as well as light locomotives and Class 142 to 144 trains. The top figure applies to all other trains.

Where the indicators show letters above the numerals, the meaning is as follows:

- HST Class 253 and 254 trains.
- MU Multiple-unit trains.
- DMU Diesel multiple-unit trains.
- EMU Electric multiple-unit trains.
- SP Sprinter trains (Class 150 to 166).
- Eurostar trains.

Complications arise where reductions of speed are necessary for two or more separate, but adjoining, permanent speed restrictions, where the warning board for the second restriction would otherwise precede the commencement sign for the first one. In such cases special arrangements apply.

The location of the warning indicator is based on the distance needed to reduce speed to the required level from the maximum permitted approach speed, based on braking curves. The distance may be extended to ensure that the associated AWS magnet is at least four seconds from any other magnet.

31. Temporary Speed Restrictions

Temporary speed restrictions (TSR for short) are imposed where the track is not in a fit condition for trains to run on at normal speed, usually pending or following maintenance or renewals. The driver is informed of such restrictions in a number of ways:

1. By an entry in the weekly operating notice, issued to all drivers, which contains a section listing all TSRs, route by route, for the area concerned.
2. By a notice in a special 'Late Notice Case' at the depot where the driver signs on duty. Drivers are required to read such notices every time they sign on duty.
3. By signs erected at the lineside, supplemented by an AWS permanent magnet.

The lineside signs are as follows:

1. A warning board, positioned on the left-hand side of the line at braking distance from the start of the TSR, and denoting the speed limit of the TSR. If it is a TSR beyond a diverging junction, the warning board will carry a directional arrow, called a directional indicator. Differential speed restrictions may apply, in which case the bottom figure showing the higher speed applies only to passenger trains (loaded or empty), postal trains and parcels trains, all composed entirely of bogie vehicles, as well as light locomotives and Class 142 to 144 trains. The lower speed applies to all other trains.
2. A speed indicator at the start of the restriction, showing the permitted speed.
3. A termination indicator at the end of the restriction.

Where the normal position of a warning board falls on the approach side of a passenger station, a siding connection or a dead-end platform line, and the speed indicator is more than 300yd ahead of that location, a repeating warning board is provided at the far end of the platform (or other appropriate location) as a reminder to the driver. The repeating warning board is a reflectorised sign with a horizontal yellow bar including two white circles and with the letter 'R' above the bar.

The warning board has horizontally placed flashing white lights which are lit at all times, and the warning board indications, the speed indicator and the termination indicator are lit during darkness (often controlled by a light-sensitive cell). Alternatively, retro-reflective boards and indicators may be used.

A portable AWS permanent magnet is placed in the 'four-foot' (ie between the rails) about 200yd on the approach side of the warning board, but where the appropriate location for the magnet falls near to a signal or its AWS magnets, it may be more convenient for warning board to be placed at the signal, and for the signal magnet to be adjusted so that only a warning indication can be given, irrespective of the aspect being shown by the signal.

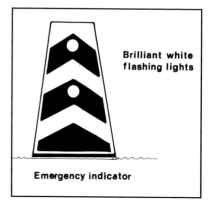

Above: **Reflectorised Repeating Warning Board at platform departure end.**

Above: **Emergency indicator for an emergency speed restriction ahead.**

Special arrangements regarding the location of warning boards, etc apply where there are two adjacent TSRs.

A TSR may be eased earlier than shown in the weekly operating notice, in which case the warning board and speed indicator will be altered to show the higher speed.

If a TSR shown in the weekly operating notice is not imposed or is withdrawn earlier than shown, the warning board, etc must be erected (or remain *in situ*) unless a special notice cancelling the TSR has been issued at least 24hr before the time it was due to start. The warning board and speed indicator must be altered to show a 'Spate' indication (see illustration).

If a TSR is withdrawn earlier than shown, or is not imposed, the speed indication in both the warning board and the speed indicator may be replaced by a Spate indicator.

Where there are TSRs on both routes at a diverging junction and the correct positions of both warning boards fall on the approach side of the junction, the second warning board must be positioned 50yd beyond the first. The second warning board will not have an AWS magnet.

The driver must not resume normal speed until he is sure that the whole of the train has passed clear of the TSR.

A missing warning board, etc, or a light out when it should be lit, must be dealt with as follows:

1. Warning board or speed indicator missing — the driver must tell the signaller at once, stopping his train specially if necessary. The signaller must tell all other drivers about it.
2. A light out at a warning board or a speed indicator — the driver must tell the signaller at once, stopping his train specially if necessary. The signaller must tell all other drivers about it. If only one light is out, and all indications are lit, the driver need not stop specially to report a failure at a warning board, nor need the signaller stop trains specially to tell drivers about it, but the driver should report it at the first convenient opportunity.
3. A termination indicator unlit — the driver must report it at the first convenient opportunity, but need not stop specially. The signaller need not stop trains specially to tell drivers about it.

If a TSR does not finish on time, it must be dealt with as an Emergency Speed Restriction.

The above description is only a general guide. Section U (part i) of the Rule Book is very comprehensive on this subject and includes 11 coloured diagrams illustrating the various permutations regarding the placing of boards, indicators and permanent magnets.

Emergency Temporary Speed Restrictions (ESRs)

When it is necessary to impose an ESR without notice to drivers, special steps must be taken to ensure that drivers

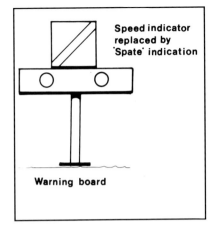

Above: A 'Spate' indicator denotes that a restriction has been withdrawn or has not been imposed.

are fully aware of it and do not fail to take their trains over the ESR at the appropriate speed. The signaller must be told at once, and equipment must be provided without delay if the restriction is to continue for more than a short time.

A Special Notice must be issued if an ESR is to continue for more than a short time.

The sequence of events after the need to impose a ESR has come to light are as follows:

1. If possible, trains should be diverted to another line or route until the equipment has been provided.
2. If it is necessary for trains to pass over the ESR before equipment is in position, the signaller must stop all trains on the line affected and explain the situation to the driver, ensuring that he correctly understands exactly where the ESR is, and the speed over it (which must not exceed 20mph). The train may then be allowed to proceed.
3. A Warning Board with associated portable AWS magnet, a Speed Indicator and a Termination Indicator must be erected under the same arrangement as for a TSR.
4. An emergency indicator must be erected 200yd on the approach side of the warning board, together with a portable AWS magnet 200yd before the emergency indicator. If the warning board is located less than ¼ mile beyond a fixed signal equipped with AWS, the emergency indicator must be erected at the signal, and the AWS electro-magnet must be disconnected so that a driver will receive a warning

irrespective of the aspect being displayed at the signal. An additional portable magnet will not then be required.

5. The emergency indicator must remain in position until details of the ESR are shown in the weekly notice or the restriction is withdrawn. The emergency indicator lights must be lit at all times. If either or both fail, the driver must tell the signaller at once, stopping specially if necessary. The signaller must inform all drivers affected.

If an ESR is more restrictive than 20mph or exceeds 1¼ miles in length (which is sometimes the case in hot weather when speeds are reduced in case of track buckling) the signaller must inform all drivers affected. He must continue to do so even when warning boards, etc have been erected, until he is told that a special notice or advice has been given to drivers.

A TSR which has a lower speed than that shown in the weekly notice, or which applies at a different time, must be treated as an ESR.

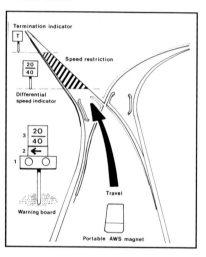

Above: **Temporary speed restriction signs: 1. Warning board; 2. Warning board applicable to a diverging line; 3. Differential speed warning board; 4. Differential speed indicator at start of restriction; 5. Termination indicator at end of restriction.**

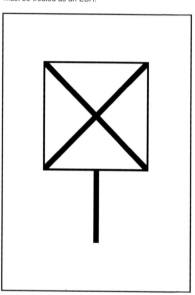

Above: Cancelling indicator for **AWS** magnet for an emergency speed restriction.

There are two quite distinct train radio systems in use on British railways. One is known as Cab Secure Radio (CSR) and the other as the National Radio Network (NRN).

Cab Secure Radio

This was designed in the late 1970s in order to be installed in those trains which were to be operated without guards, now known as 'driver-only operation' (DOO), because the provision of this type of radio system was one of the safety requirements agreed between the BRB and the Railway Inspectorate for the operation of suburban passenger trains without guards. It is now used more generally and forms the normal method of communication between driver and signaller.

The other main requirements for DOO operation are that the line must be equipped with continuous train detection equipment and multiple-aspect colour light signalling. For technical reasons, the line must be controlled by a signalbox equipped with modern train describer equipment.

The boundaries between radio areas are indicated by lineside signs, and when a train passes one of these signs the radio channel in use on the train is changed automatically.

Method of Operation

When a train enters traffic, or changes its train description number, the driver must send a data message to a management processor in the controlling signalbox, which states the number of the signal at which the train is standing. The call number of the train's radio equipment (known as the train stock number) is automatically included in this message so that the call number can automatically be correlated with the train description number. This is necessary because the signaller does not know the call number of any particular train and must use the train description number to obtain radio communication with a driver. Similarly, when the driver wishes to speak to the signaller he operates his radio to send a call signal to the signalbox, which is indicated to the signaller by the train description number of that train appearing on a visual display unit (VDU). Incoming calls are queued, but if a driver makes an emergency call this is shown separately on the VDU and the signaller must respond urgently. The driver cannot speak until the signaller opens the communication channel, but the signaller can initiate a call to a driver at any time. All calls are recorded.

The signaller can ascertain at once from his signalling control panel where the train is, by looking for the train description number. Strict radio procedures are followed, although the system is designed to ensure that the signaller knows which driver he is speaking to. The radio messages between the signaller and a driver cannot be overheard by other drivers, therefore there is no danger of another driver acting upon an instruction from the signaller that is not meant for him, but the signaller can, if he wishes, broadcast a general message to all drivers in a particular area. The signaller can also speak to the passengers in a train over the train's public address system.

A feature of CSR, incorporated with driver-only operation in mind, is that if the driver leaves the DSD treadle up for longer than a minute with the direction selector switch in forward, or does not react properly to a vigilance alarm for a similar time, the radio will automatically send an alarm message to the signaller, on the assumption that the driver has become unwell and needs assistance urgently.

The National Radio Network (NRN)

The National Radio Network (NRN) was first installed about 1980 to provide radio communication between the radio control office and men out on the line and allow the more efficient management of engineer's possessions of the line. It also enabled electrification telephones on AC overhead electric lines to be removed. The system took a long time to reach its full potential due to the unreliability of the software and inadequate radio coverage, but additional base stations have been provided to give almost complete coverage of the railway system. NRN also provides radio communication with the railway ETD telephone system.

The advantages of having radio communication with trains are obvious, but the high cost of cab secure radio and the technical difficulties of installing it nationwide meant that thoughts turned to the possibility of using or adapting the National Radio Network for the purpose, and this was done. Driving cabs are now equipped with some form of radio.

Calls from driving cabs must be made only in the following circumstances:

1. The train has failed, or has a defect, and needs assistance or technical examination, or the driver needs technical advice.
2. When the Rules require the driver to report to the

signaller his presence at a signal but the telephone has failed or there is a sign indicating limited safety clearance.

3. Giving or asking for information concerning train working, delays, connectional arrangements, etc.
4. During engineering work, when agreed.
5. In an emergency (see below).

If the signaller is unable to call the driver direct he must arrange via a third party for the driver to call him.

NRN is not classed as a secure radio system, since there is no correlation between the train's radio call number and the train description number. The signaller is not normally aware of the radio call number of a particular train, and the radio traffic is normally initiated by drivers. Therefore, for normal communication in NRN territory the lineside and signalpost telephones must be used as they indicate the actual location of the driver.

Boundaries between NRN radio zones are indicated by a lineside sign, and the driver must reset the radio when passing one of these signs.

Use of Radio by Signaller in an Emergency
When the Train Signalling Regulations require the signaller to stop a train in an emergency, the signaller must use radio if this might enable the train to be stopped more quickly. He must also carry out the Regulation concerned. In most cases this call will need to be made via the Railtrack Control Office, who will be able to put out an emergency call to all trains within that NRN radio base station coverage area.

The Emergency Call Procedure
A driver can use his train radio to obtain access to the railway telephone network and he can make an emergency call by pressing a red button, which connects him immediately with a railway traffic control office. The control office receiving the emergency call can broadcast a message to all trains within a particular base station radio coverage area, which will be heard over the loudspeaker in driving compartments. The opportunity for avoiding a mishap, or a further mishap, is thus enhanced.

The emergency call procedure must be used only when it is necessary for other trains to be stopped or cautioned owing to an accident or obstruction or other exceptional incident, or when the emergency services are needed.

If the driver has used the emergency call procedure and is unable to speak directly to the signaller but only to a third party, he must:

1. Stop his train at once and tell the signaller, using a signalpost telephone.
2. Carry out any protection of the line which is necessary.

Making an emergency call cuts off all normal calls and connects the caller immediately with Operations Control.

Global System for Mobile Communication — Railways (GSM-R)
GSM-R is a European Community initiative to provide a new digital communication system for current and future railway applications, including train control and voice communication. It will form the 'message carrier' for ETCS Levels 2 and 3. German Railways (Deutsche Bahn AG) signed a GSM-R contract in 1999 for equipping 27,000km of track by 2002, and the system will ultimately be extended over the European network, including Britain.

Whilst GSM-R may be little known at present, its objectives are extensive:

- Integration of mobile radio communication in place of eight analogue radio systems.
- Reduction of signalling equipment.
- Fewer lineside signals.
- Fewer track circuits and axle counters.
- Fewer different train control systems.
- Dissemination of information about timetables, ticketing, reservations, etc.

There are many other potential applications.

Radio Area Boundary Signal - Cab Secure Radio

Similar Sign for the National Rail Network with the letters NRN

PART 9

33. Engineering Operations on the Line

From time to time, the line may become unsafe from a variety of causes, such as landslip, flooding and washout, or when it is under repair or renewal, and it is necessary to ensure that no train can enter such a piece of line. The arrangements for ensuring the safety of trains are of three kinds:

1. Protection when the line is unsafe.
2. Protection of engineering work which is not being carried out under an Engineer's Possession.
3. Protection of engineering work being carried out under an Engineer's Possession.

Protection when the Line is Unsafe

When the line is unsafe for trains to run upon it three things must be done immediately:

1. A track circuit operating clip must be placed on the line to place signals to danger.
2. Detonator protection must be provided.
3. The signaller must be told as quickly as possible, so that he can place signals to danger.

Detonator protection consists of placing three detonators on the line, 20yd apart, 1¼ miles away. However, the three detonators must be placed on the line immediately, before reaching that distance, in the following circumstances:

1. If a train approaches.
2. If the person carrying out the duty reaches a signalbox or telephone communicating with a signalbox before then, in which case the detonators need not be placed at the full distance if the signaller advises that protection is being given by signals.
3. After switching a signal to danger by means of a signalpost replacement switch.
4. Before entering a tunnel. If the 1¼-mile point falls within the tunnel, the detonators must be placed at the far end of it.
5. Just before a trailing junction. Both legs of the junction have to be protected and it is a question of judgement as to which is done first.

The person concerned must remain at the detonators showing a red flag or lamp until the line is again safe for trains to pass.

Protection of Engineering Work Not Carried Out Under Engineer's Possession

The work should be planned in advance wherever possible to minimise interference with the running of trains. The person responsible for arranging protection must be qualified to do so and is known as the Protection Controller (PC), or the Controller of Site Safety (COSS) if there is no PC. He must make appropriate arrangements with the signaller and will be given an Authority Number. One of the following protection procedures must be carried out:

1. Place a Track Circuit Operating Device (T-COD) on the track. The signaller must check that the track circuit concerned is initially clear but shows occupied when the T-COD is applied.

Right: **Possession limit board used during engineering possessions.** *D. C. Hall*

PROTECTION ARRANGEMENTS FOR ENGINEERING POSSESSIONS

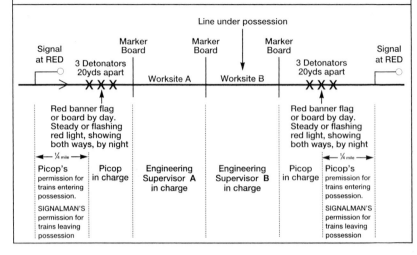

2. Disconnect the protecting signal so that it can show only a 'Stop' aspect, but only if competent and certificated to do so.

3. Send out a handsignaller with detonators under arrangements similar to those which apply when the line is unsafe.

These arrangements may also be used to safeguard anyone working on or near the line who may be endangered by passing trains, or when cranes or other mechanical equipment which may foul the line are being used.

Whilst the principles of protection are essentially simple, the detailed instructions regarding the provision and removal of protection are complex, in order to ensure safety. They include the detailed arrangements for passing trains through the area during the work, and are set out in Section T (part ii) of the Rule Book.

Protection of Engineering Work Under Engineer's Possession

These arrangements are normally used whenever engineering operations are to be carried out using engineer's trains or on-track equipment or machinery. There may be several work sites within one possession, which may extend for several miles, although the length of line under possession must be kept to the minimum as the normal signalling arrangements are suspended. No train other than an engineer's train may pass through a possession.

The arrangements for ensuring safety are detailed and lengthy, and fall under the following headings:

1. The appointment of specific people with special responsibilities.
2. The protection of the possession.
3. Controlling the movement of trains from the 'live' railway into the area of the possession.
4. Protection of individual worksites.
5. Controlling the movement of trains within the possession.
6. Controlling the movement of trains from the possession into the 'live' railway.
7. Giving up the possession.

(The word 'train' includes engineer's on-track equipment and machinery.)

1. Appointment of Specific People

• Person in Charge of the Possession (PICOP) must be certified as competent and familiar with the line and the arrangements. Must normally have no other responsibilities. Wears an appropriately worded armband.

• Engineering Supervisor in charge of each work site. Wears an appropriately worded armband.

2. Protection of the Possession

This is given by fixed signals and detonators (three, 20yd apart) at both ends of the possession. The detonators in rear of the possession are generally placed ¼ mile beyond the protecting signal. Those at the other end of the possession are generally placed ¼ mile before a stop signal. A possession limit board is placed in the four-foot next to the centre detonator. It is red, with the word 'STOP', on both sides, and has a steady or flashing red light visible along the line in both directions. The protection is intended not only to prevent a train from straying wrongly into the possession but also to prevent a train from straying from inside the possession on to the 'live' railway.

3. Trains Entering the Possession
The signaller must not allow a train to proceed towards the protecting detonators from either end without the PICOP's permission. Having obtained it, he must tell the driver what is happening and instruct him to pass the protecting signal at danger and proceed cautiously to the protecting detonators, from which point the PICOP will authorise the next movement.

4. Protection of Individual Worksites
Individual worksites must be indicated by marker boards except where there are no engineer's trains or on-track machines within the possession or there is only one worksite and the only movements are on-track machines. The marker boards are double-sided and have two flashing lights, vertically arranged. Red lights indicate the entrance to the worksite — the board is not to be passed unless the Engineering Supervisor authorises it. Yellow lights indicate the exit from the worksite — the board is not to be passed without the PICOP's authority. The boards are positioned at least 100yd from each end of the worksite.

5. Movements Within the Possession
As the normal signalling arrangements are suspended in a possession, all movements must be authorised verbally. The only people authorised to do so are the PICOP and the Engineering Supervisors. Movements within a worksite are authorised by the Engineering Supervisor. All other movements are authorised by the PICOP. Propelling movements are allowed under special conditions. This part of the possession arrangements needs very careful handling in view of the variety of movements and hazards that can occur, and especially as possessions are customarily carried out at night. Trains may move in either direction, they may be split into one or more sections, they may be propelled, they may be stationary, there may be noisy machinery, and there are likely to be a large number of men at work both on the trains and on the track.

6. Movements Leaving the Possession
The PICOP must tell the signaller when any movement is ready to leave the possession. Authority for such a movement is then given by the signaller.

7. Giving up the Possession
This is one of the most critical activities, as it is essential to ensure that all trains, machines and equipment have been removed from the possession, that all men on site are aware that the possession is being given up, and that the line is safe for trains to run on. This is the PICOP's responsibility and he will receive a written certificate from each Engineering Supervisor to that effect. He can then tell the signaller that he is ready to give up the possession and remove the protection.

General Notes
There are special arrangements where level crossings are concerned:

- A number of documents and certificates are maintained and completed.
- The signaller makes specific entries in his train register book.

Note: The contents of this chapter are intended to be only a brief summary of the arrangements. They are set out in great detail in Section T (part iii) of the Rule Book.

Below: **Interior of Feltham power signalbox.** *IAL*

PART 10

34. Channel Tunnel Signalling

General Description

The signalling system installed in the Channel Tunnel is known as the TVM 430 system. It is a French system and is similar in principle to the system installed on the TGV Nord high-speed line from Paris to Calais. There are no lineside colour light signals and the driver is informed of the speed at which he is to travel, or whether he is required to stop, by the display of information in his driving cab.

Track Equipment

The lines are track-circuited throughout and are divided into 500m (approx 550yd) blocks or sections, with a marker board at the end of each block to provide a reference point for the driver. Transmission of information to the train is achieved by means of coded track circuits via the running rails.

Train Equipment

The traction unit receives coded information from the track circuits about the state of the line ahead, and an on-board processor calculates the maximum speed at which the train may travel, including a braking curve if a reduction of speed is necessary. The speed of the train is controlled by the driver, but if he exceeds the maximum permitted speed or strays outside the braking curve the brakes will be applied. The principle is very similar to that adopted for the Automatic Train Protection system installed on two lines in Britain, the difference being in the means of transmission of information from the track to the train.

Train Controls

The signalling control system is based on the maintenance of a number of unoccupied 500m blocks in front of a train. Braking from the top speed of 160km/h (100mph) requires four blocks, and an additional 'buffer' block is provided in case of accidental overrun.

The main control centre for the Channel Tunnel is located at Folkestone, but there is a control centre in France at Coquelles which can take over the tunnel control if Folkestone were to be out of action for any reason. The Folkestone Control Centre has a geographical panel 25yd long showing the location of all trains. Automatic Route Setting is employed on a large scale.

Right: **The modern Railway. A Class 373 Channel Tunnel train passes a Class 465 electric multiple unit.**
Brian Morrison

The development of signalling technology, both by the railway undertakings themselves and by the national and international signalling contractors, has been a continuous process, although its application to Britain's railways has been marked by a series of major advances:

1. The application of electric power to the operation of points.
2. The introduction of the electrically lit colour light signal.
3. The invention of the track circuit.
4. The replacement of mechanical interlocking by electrical relay interlocking.
5. The one-control switch (OCS) system of setting a route and clearing signals, allowing one signalbox to control large areas.

6. The refinement of the OCS system into the entrance-exit (NX) system, which became the BR standard in the 1960s.
7. The application of solid-state computer technology to signalling interlocking, replacing relays.
8. The adoption of visual display units in signalling centre operating rooms, replacing the large indications panels.
9. The use of tracker-balls and keyboards, instead of push-buttons on large control panels, for use by the signaller in controlling points and signals.
10. The use of radio for vital signalling messages, as in the Radio Electronic Token Block system.
11. The application of computers to the automation of route-setting.

The speed at which modern signalling developments are adopted depends on a number of factors, such as:

- The availability of finance.
- The capital cost of new equipment.

Below: **The Preston station section on the panel in Preston power signalbox.**

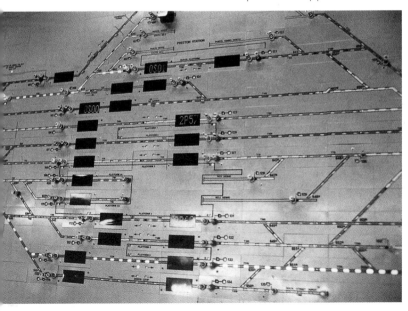

- The benefits it might provide in greater reliability and reduced maintenance and operating costs.
- The need for increased line capacity to cater for traffic growth.
- The need for improved safety levels.

The factors which lead to existing signalling being replaced in more modern form are:

1. Existing equipment becoming life-expired.
2. Electrification schemes, which normally entail major resignalling, both for technical reasons and to cater for higher speeds and altered track layouts.
3. Changes in traffic patterns and levels, leading to the need either to reduce signalling costs or to cater for increased traffic levels.
4. Conurbation area schemes for improved passenger train services, frequently promoted by local authorities and passenger transport executives.
5. The desire of train operators for higher speeds.

So far as main and suburban lines are concerned, the standard which has now been adopted is the Integrated Electronic Control Centre (IECC), comprised of solid-state interlocking, visual display units and tracker-ball/keyboard for use by the signaller, and Automatic Route Setting (ARS). ARS is likely to become much more widespread as train services become more regular and reliable. It produces a more predictable response and is capable of being programmed to make the optimum decisions in the event of interruptions to the service arising from late running, cancellations and mishaps, etc.

There remain several thousand miles of double-track secondary line, much of it still mechanically signalled and worked under the traditional Absolute Block System. Traffic levels do not justify the cost of continuous track circuiting and colour light signalling but much of the equipment is at, or nearing, the end of its life. Replacement on a like-for-like basis is not really an option, because on the one hand new mechanical interlocking frames are becoming very difficult to obtain, and on the other hand the technical expertise needed to install and maintain them and other signalling equipment is becoming equally rare, and expensive to provide.

The normal solution would be the use of small local panels operating colour light signals in locations where there are a number of points, and with the interlocking being performed either by relays or by solid-state equipment. The expense of installing track circuits over long lengths of open line can be avoided by the use of axle counters. Often the major cost in a resignalling scheme is the lineside cabling connecting the equipment to a signalbox, and providing communication between one signalbox and another.

So far as the resignalling of secondary lines is concerned, no simple, cheap and efficient substitute for the Absolute Block System has yet been found, but it is entirely possible that ETCS Levels 2 or 3 might ultimately provide the answer, especially when most trains have been equipped with ETCS for use on other routes. Lineside signalboxes and signals would not be required, nor any form of track-based train detection system. Line capacity would be increased and train working would become more efficient. Here is a challenge for the signalling industry.

Track circuits are required not only as part of the signalling system but also to allow the automation of manned level crossings, most of which are situated on secondary lines. The automation of level crossings must continue, because of the savings in manpower costs. It also leads to improved safety levels and allows signalling installations to be simplified. The pace of the modernisation of level crossings has slowed in recent years, and can proceed only as quickly as the availability of finance and technical resources (including staff) allow. The latter is likely to be the limiting factor.

Urgent steps need to be taken to ensure a sufficient supply of suitably qualified staff in the future to carry out the work. The situation is not helped by peaks and troughs of work in the signalling industry. It is likely to be a major problem if action is not taken quickly, and there is an equal responsibility on Network Rail to ensure that there is a smooth programme of work. That is in everyone's interests. Signalling contractors need to ensure a smooth flow of recruits into the industry, but that will happen only if there is a reasonable degree of certainty about the future workload. It is not so long ago that signalling contractors were shedding staff owing to a workload famine. Here is a challenge for the Rail Industry Training Council and the professional institutions to provide the focus.

Track circuits themselves have now reached the limit of their technical development and they are becoming increasingly unreliable in the detection of certain types of modern multiple-units under the adverse conditions experienced during the leaf-fall season. Particular problems have been encountered with Class 158 units even when fitted with track circuit shunt assisters. The unreliability of track circuits causes train delays, which affects the punctuality and reliability of the train service. Consideration is therefore being given to alternative methods of train detection, eg the use of axle counters, but track circuits have other benefits in addition to their main purpose of train detection. Track circuits can:

- Protect the line by the use of a track circuit operating clip.
- Detect the presence of an obstruction.
- Detect a broken rail in some circumstances.
- Hold points in position.

There may prove to be no alternative to the use of track circuits in congested station areas.

Radio can provide an answer in certain cases, but the detection of broken rails in the absence of track circuits is

Above: **The modern way: VDU screen, tracker-ball and keyboard at Willesden.** *GEC-General Signal Ltd*

Inset: **The control room of the modern Integrated Electronic Control Centre (IECC) at Ashford.** *GEC-General Signal Ltd*

a challenge for the permanent way engineer. He already has to cope with single-rail track circuits on overhead electrified lines.

A major development in signalling and train control philosophy is now taking place – the European Rail Traffic Management System (ERTMS) incorporating the European Train Control System (ETCS). Under European Union regulations its use on Britain's high-speed lines will be required, but ultimately its use on other lines has the potential to bring cost benefits, and improvements in efficiency and safety. ETCS in its most advanced modes does not require the use of lineside signals nor track-based train detection systems, which are expensive to install and maintain and are not free from right-side failures, which cause train delays. However, the development processes are proving more prolonged and difficult than was initially envisaged.

The purpose-built high-speed lines in France used by the TGVs, and the line through the Channel Tunnel, have no lineside signals, and all the instructions to drivers are picked up from coded messages in the running rails and displayed on the driver's control desk.

Automatic control of the driving of trains is already in operation on certain Metro lines in Britain and abroad, but whether such a system would ever be applied to the driving of main line trains is questionable. A driver is required for other purposes besides the normal driving of the train, and these might be listed as:

- Keeping a lookout for men working on the track, and sounding the horn to warn them of the train's approach.

- Keeping a lookout and sounding the horn when approaching level crossings.
- Keeping a lookout for anything that might hazard trains (his own or others), such as:
    Flood damage;
    Bridge damage caused by road vehicles;
    Obstructions on the line, either accidental or deliberate;
    Defective track;
    Animals on the line.
- Being on hand to deal with traction failures.
- Working through a section under caution for a whole variety of reasons, eg signalling and track circuit failures, defective track, vandalism, obstructions, animals on the line, examination of the line, etc.

There is little point in automating the driving of trains unless the cost of the driver can be avoided, and, as it seems likely, for the reasons given above, that drivers will continue to be required for purposes other than normal driving, there is little likelihood of any train operator incurring heavy expenditure in automating the driving of trains, except perhaps in special situations.

Based therefore on the retention of drivers, there was a need to modernise or replace the Automatic Warning System (AWS), and a new system, the Train Protection and Warning System (TPWS) was designed as an overlay to AWS. TPWS initiates an irreversible emergency stop if train approaches a Red signal, a buffer stop or a speed restriction too fast for safety, or passes a signal at Danger. TPWS has been installed at about 40% of signals, at locations where the risk of collision or derailment following a SPAD or too high a speed is particularly high. Installation was completed at the end of 2003.

TPWS has brought a substantial increase in safety. It was initially regarded as a stopgap until ETCS could be installed, but that is now likely to be several years ahead. Indeed, the increase in safety that ETCS would bring is now considered fairly marginal, and installation would have to be based mainly on a strong financial case. And the availability of funds.

In the second issue of this booklet, an action agenda for the railway and signalling industries was suggested, which included the following items:

1. An improved AWS system which can overcome a driver's failure to obey a warning.
2. The resignalling of the West Coast main line in whatever form can be afforded.
3. A cheaper system of signalling secondary lines.
4. A new train detection and locating system, either in addition to, or in replacement of, track circuits.

TPWS, ETCS and axle counters can provide the answers to all four items.

And today's action agenda?

1. Press on with all speed with the development of ETCS, because of its many benefits, including greater safety.
2. Abolish the driver's reliance on lineside signals. It is unsatisfactory that the railway industry has entered the 21st century still requiring the driver to peer out of his cab window in all weathers to locate and identify his signal, when the technology exists to provide on the console in his driving cab all the information he needs to drive his train safely.
3. Ensure that the driver is given sufficient information about a diverging junction ahead to enable him to take his train through the junction at the required speed without premature and excessive braking, and with full knowledge of the state of the line ahead. Adoption of the speed-signalling philosophy is a major step in this direction.
4. Find an alternative method to track circuits for detecting broken rails.

The railway industry stands on the threshold of what could well be one of the most exciting periods in its history. It must not fail to grasp the opportunity.

Now that collisions and derailments caused by SPADs and overspeeding have been considerably reduced by the installation of TPWS, the outstanding safety issue is becoming the interaction of trains and road vehicles, not merely at level crossings but also at bridges both under and over the railway. It is not possible to eliminate collisions between road vehicles and trains, but more needs to be done to improve the front-end protection of trains, incorporating obstruction deflectors to avoid trains becoming derailed after a collision with a road vehicle. Highway Authorities too need to be more pro-active to prevent the escape of road vehicles from the road, on to the railway.

Right: **Multiple-aspect colour light signal No L3971 at Shipley, with SPAD indicator signal 50yd beyond, protecting the junction to Bradford.** *Author*

Glossary of Technical Terms and Abbreviations

Absolute Block — A signalling system which allows only one train to be between two signalboxes on the same line at the same time.

Acceptance of a train — A term used in Absolute Block signalling when a signalman allows a train to proceed towards his signalbox.

Accommodation Level Crossing —A private level crossing connecting land separated by the railway.

Advance — Further along in the direction of travel.

Annunciator — A buzzer which sounds when a train occupies a berth track circuit with the home signal at danger.

Approach control — A colour light junction signal which is held at red although the line ahead may be clear, in order to ensure that the driver slows down for a speed-restricted turnout.

Approach locking — A system of locking facing points so that they cannot be moved across in front of an approaching train.

Approach release — The point at which an approach-controlled signal is released.

Aspect — The colour displayed by a colour light signal.

Automatic Barrier Crossing (ABCL) — A level crossing whose operation is monitored by the train driver.

Automatic Half-barrier Level Crossing (AHB) — An automatically-operated level crossing.

Automatic Open Crossing (AOCL) — A level crossing without barriers whose road traffic signals are monitored by the driver.

Automatic Route Setting (ARS) — A computerised system for setting routes according to a pre-programmed formula.

Automatic Section — An automatically-signalled section on an Absolute Block line.

Automatic signal — A signal which is operated by the passage of trains.

Automatic Train Control (ATC) — A former safety device for warning a driver of the need to slow down or stop.

Automatic Train Protection (ATP) — A safety system for ensuring that the driver slows down or stops when necessary.

Automatic Warning System (AWS) — A safety device for warning a driver to slow down or stop.

Axle Counters — Track-mounted equipment which counts the number of axles on a train.

Back board — Drivers' name for a distant signal.

Banner Repeating Signal — A signal which gives a driver advance information about a signal which has a limited sighting distance.

Berth Track Circuit — Track circuit in rear of home signal.

Block bell — The bell used for sending bell codes between adjacent manual signalboxes.

Block indicator — An instrument indicating the state of the line between adjacent manual signalboxes.

Blocking Back — Term used in Absolute Block when an unsignalled train or shunting movement is to be allowed to stand within the clearing point or outside the home signal.

Block section — In Absolute Block, the section of line between the Section Signal of one signalbox and the Home Signal of the next signalbox ahead.

Block signalling — A system of signalling based on block sections.

Block switch — Enables a signalbox to be closed by putting the signalboxes on each side into through communication with each other.

Block telephone — A telephone link between two adjacent manual signalboxes, using the block telegraph wires.

Braking distance — The distance a train needs in which to stop.

Bridge bashing — Overheight road vehicles colliding with railway bridges over the road.

Calling-on signal — To allow a train into an occupied section.

Cat's eyes — A railwayman's term for the 'proceed' aspect of a position light signal.

Classification of Trains — A list of the different categories of train.

Clear signal — A colour light signal displaying a green aspect, or a semaphore stop signal in the 'Off' position.

Clearing a signal — The action of the signalman in changing a signal from 'danger' to a proceed aspect.

Clearing point — The point to which the line must be clear before a train can be accepted from the signalbox in rear under the Absolute Block system of signalling.

Closed Circuit Television (CCTV) — Equipment used for remote monitoring or supervisory purposes.

Coaching stock — Vehicles designed to be capable of running in passenger trains.

Colour light area — An area in which all signals are of the colour light type and usually worked under the Track Circuit Block system.

Colour light signal — A signal which conveys its message by means of coloured lights.

Controlled signal — A colour light signal which is cleared from red by the signalman.

Cut-out sign — Metal cut-out numerals erected at the lineside to denote the permitted speed.

Delayed yellow — Allows a train to enter a colour light section without the full overlap being available.

Detection — A means of ensuring that facing points are correctly closed before the signal can be cleared.

Detonators — Small disc-shaped warning devices, placed on the rail head, which explode when a train passes over them.

Distant arm proving — A means of ensuring that the distant signal arm is in the 'On' position before the block indicator can be placed to 'Line clear'.

Distant signal — A signal which tells the driver whether he needs to be prepared to stop at the next signal.

Double-yellow aspect — A preliminary caution signal in four-aspect colour light signalling.

Down — All running lines and trains are assigned a direction, either Up or Down. The Up direction is usually towards London or a main centre. Trains using lines which are signalled for both directions are either Up or Down, according to their individual direction.

Driver's Reminder Appliance — A device in the driving cab which enables the driver to set a reminder that the signal ahead is at danger.

Electric token block — A system of signalling used on single lines.

Electronic token — Used in Radio Electronic Token Block.

Emergency Indicator — A sign used to inform a driver of a speed restriction imposed without prior notice.

Emergency replacement switch (ERS) — A switch that enables a signalman to replace an automatic signal to danger in an emergency.

Entrance-Exit System (NX) — A system of route-setting used in modern power signalboxes.

ERTMS — The European Railway Train Management System (see Chapter 22).

ETCS — European Train Control System (see Chapter 22)

Examination of line — A method of establishing whether it is safe to run trains through a section.

Facing point — A point which can change the direction of a train approaching it.

Facing point lock — Equipment for ensuring that facing points cannot move irregularly.

Fail-safe — Signalling equipment is designed so that any failures will result in signals being set at danger, hence 'fail-safe'.

Fast line — Where there are four separate tracks, one pair of Up and Down lines may be called the Fast lines and the other pair the Slow lines.

Fixed signal — A signal in a fixed location. The word 'fixed' refers to the location and not to the aspect or indication of the signal.

Flank protection — Additional signal and point interlocking at junctions, for extra safety.

Flashing yellow aspects — Warn the driver that he is routed over a speed-restricted turnout at a junction ahead.

Fouling bar — Equipment used to establish that a vehicle is safely clear of the fouling point.

Fouling point — The precise spot where a vehicle standing at a converging point between two lines will come into contact with a vehicle on the other line.

Four-aspect territory — An area where all signals can display four aspects (red, one yellow, two yellows, or green).

Four-foot — Railway term for the space between the two running rails of a line.

Goods line — A line which is not signalled and equipped to the standard needed for passenger trains.

Green aspect — Means that the line ahead is clear and that the next signal will not be at red (or at single yellow in four-aspect territory).

Ground Frame — A stage or cabin containing switches or levers for controlling points and signals, but which can only be used when released by the controlling signalbox.

GSM-R — Global System for Mobile Communication — Railway (see Chapter 32).

Half-cock — Term used by drivers to describe a semaphore signal that is halfway between 'On' and 'Off'.

Handshake — Simultaneous successful operation of separate electronic devices in the same system.

Handsignalman — Person stationed at the lineside to give signals to the driver by flag or lamp.

Headway — The minimum distance between two trains travelling in the same direction that will enable green signals to be given to the driver of the second train and enable him to travel at unrestricted speed.

Home normal contact (HNC) — A means of ensuring that the home signal lever is replaced in the frame before 'Line clear' can be given.

Home signal — In Absolute Block, the first (or outermost) stop signal on the approach to a signalbox. May also be called Outer Home or Home No 1 where there are two Home signals.

Hot axlebox detector (HABD) — Apparatus for detecting an overheated axlebox on a rail vehicle.

Hudd system of ATC — A former system of warning the driver of the need to slow down or stop.

Illuminated diagram — A panel in a signalbox containing a diagrammatic representation of the track under the signalman's control and with certain functions, such as the location of trains, being shown by lights.

Integrated Electronic Control Centre (IECC) — The most modern type of signalbox, with visual display units instead of control panels, and with routes being set by tracker-ball or keyboard instead of push-button. They have solid-state interlocking controls and Automatic Route Setting.

Intermediate Block Section (IBS) — An additional unstaffed block section between two Absolute Block signalboxes, generally worked from the rear signalbox.

Isolate — Take equipment out of use.

Junction indicator — Displayed at a junction signal to inform the driver which way a junction is set.

King lever — A lever whose operation unlocks other levers.

Lamp proving — A system of ensuring that a lamp in a colour light signal is lit before the next signal in rear can show a proceed aspect.

Lever collar — Piece of equipment placed over a lever to prevent it from physically being moved.

Light-emitting diode (LED) — Provides a tiny bright light when illuminated.

Line — A loose term which can mean just one pair of rails, eg the Up line, or may mean all the tracks on a route.

Line clear — The position of the block indicator when a

signalman has accepted a train.

Line speed — The maximum permitted speed of a line.

Main aspect — The red, yellow, double-yellow or green aspect of a colour light signal.

Manually-controlled Barriers (MCB) — A manned level crossing with barriers.

Manual signalbox — A signalbox in which the signal- and points-operating levers are pulled over and replaced by physical effort.

Miniature Warning Lights (MWL) — Small red and green lights at certain types of level crossing.

Multiple-aspect signal — A colour light signal capable of displaying three or four aspects.

Nearside — The left-hand side in the direction of travel.

Normal — Denotes the usual position in which points lie.

No Signaller Token System (NST) — A method of working trains over a single line with a signalman at only one end of the section.

NX System — See 'Entrance-Exit System'.

Occupation Level Crossing — A private level crossing, usually giving access between premises and a public road.

Occupied — Denotes the presence of a train.

Off — A proceed aspect in a colour light signal, or a semaphore signal arm inclined at 45°.

Off-side — The right-hand side in the direction of travel.

On — A red aspect in a colour light signal, or a semaphore signal arm in the horizontal position.

One-control switch system (OCS) — A route setting signalling system in which a point and the junction signal are set by turning the appropriate switch.

One-Train Working (OTW) — A method of working a single line by confining it to one train at a time.

Open Level Crossing — An unmanned crossing without road traffic signals.

Out of correspondence — Denotes that points are not correctly set.

Overlap — A section of line beyond a signal which, for safety reasons, must be clear before the next signal in rear can show a proceed aspect.

Passenger line — One signalled and equipped for use by passenger trains.

Permanent speed restriction (PSR) — A restriction imposed owing to sharp curves or other permanent cause.

Permissive Block System — A signalling system which allows more than one train to be in a section on the same line at the same time.

Pilotman — A person appointed to conduct trains over a single line or a line being used for trains in both directions, during failure of equipment or repairs, or owing to an obstruction.

Platform starting signal — A stop signal at the departure end of a passenger station platform.

Position Light Ground Signal (PLGS) — A signal on the ground, controlling shunting movements. *Position Light Signal (PLS)* — A signal located on the same post as a colour light running signal, and fixed below it. It controls train movements other than normal running movements.

Power signalbox (PSB) — A signalbox in which points and signals are operated by electric or other power and controlled by switch or push-button. Interlocking between points and signals is performed by electric relays. PSBs usually cover large areas, and have large control and indications panels.

Proceed aspect — A green, yellow or double-yellow light shown at a colour light signal, which means that the driver may proceed past it.

Protection of the line — Warning action taken to stop trains running into an obstruction, a failed train or other source of danger.

Radio Electronic Token Block (RETB) — A signalling system used on single lines.

Rear — Behind, in the direction of travel, ie a section of line which a train has already travelled over.

Red aspect — Danger, stop. Displayed by a colour light signal.

Reminder appliance — Used in manual signalling to remind a signalman of the presence of a train or other circumstance.

Repeater — A dial or indicator in a manual signalbox, showing the position of a signal arm and whether the signal lamp is lit.

Reverse — Denotes that points are lying in a position opposite to normal.

Rotary block — A special type of block instrument, used in some former Midland Railway signalboxes.

Route-relay interlocking — A system of interlocking between points and signals, performed by electric relays.

Ruling gradient — The main or most important gradient on a section of line with more than one gradient.

Running line — Any line other than a siding. Train movements on running lines are controlled by fixed signals.

Running movement — A normal train movement on a running line, under the control of a running signal.

Running signal — A main aspect in a colour light signal, or a distant or stop semaphore signal.

Section signal — In Absolute Block, the most advanced stop signal (ie the signal which admits a train to the block section ahead).

Semaphore signal — A fixed signal, whose meaning is given to drivers by the position of an oblong arm during daylight, and by coloured lights at night.

Semi-automatic signal — A colour light signal which is worked automatically by the passage of trains, but which can also be controlled from a signalbox or ground frame.

Sequential locking — Interlocking between signal levers to ensure that they are pulled over in the correct sequence.

Service brake application — The normal brake application which is made by a driver in routine service (as opposed to an emergency application).

Setting back — Denotes a short-distance shunting movement, usually in the wrong direction.

Shunt-ahead signal — Allows a driver to pass a stop signal by a short distance for shunting purposes.

Shunt frame — Similar to a ground frame, but often a former signalbox.

Shunt movement — A short-distance movement, often setting

back through points, and controlled by shunting signals.

Sighting distance — The maximum distance at which a driver can see a signal ahead of him.

Signalling panel — A panel in a signalbox giving a diagrammatic representation of the layout under the signalman's control, together with control switches or push-buttons and track circuit etc indications.

Signalpost replacement switch — A switch at the foot of an automatic colour light signal, which enables the signal to be switched to, and maintained at, red by the use of a key.

Signalpost telephone (SPT) — A telephone provided at a signal for the driver to speak to the signalman.

Six-foot — A term for the space between the Up and Down lines.

Slack — A term for a temporary speed restriction.

Slotting — A mechanism for controlling semaphore signal arms where two signalboxes are involved.

Slow line — A name often used for one of a pair of lines, eg the Up Slow line, where there are four lines of way (see 'Fast line').

Solid-state interlocking — A computerised software system for controlling the interlocking between points and signals.

SPAD — Signal Passed at Danger without Authority.

SPAD signal — A signal which is normally unlit but which flashes when a driver passes a signal at danger without authority about 50yd in rear.

Spate indicator — Used in connection with temporary speed restrictions.

Speed indicator — A sign erected at the running-on end of a temporary speed restriction.

Splitting distants — Two distant signals erected side by side, to tell a driver in advance which way he is routed at the junction ahead.

Staff (or train staff) — A form of token used in the working of a single line.

Staff and ticket working — An obsolete form of controlling the working of trains over a single line.

Starting signal — See 'Section signal'.

Station limits — The section of line between the outermost home signal and the most advanced stop signal worked from the same signalbox.

Station working — Special regulations governing shunting movements within station limits.

Stop signal — A signal capable of showing a stop aspect or indication.

Subsidiary signal — In semaphore signalling, a calling-on or shunt-ahead signal.

Sunflower — Drivers' name for the AWS visual indicator.

Sykes Lock and Block signalling — A former method of signalling.

Temporary speed restriction (TSR) — A speed restriction imposed for a short period.

Termination indicator — A sign at the running-off end of a temporary speed restriction.

Token — A physical object, eg a tablet, staff or key, used in the Electric Token method of signalling single lines.

Tokenless block — A method of working single lines without using a token.

Track — A term which loosely includes the rails and sleepers, or generically as in 'track and signalling'.

Track circuit — An electrically-operated train detection device, which uses the running rails.

Track Circuit Block (TCB) — A method of working trains over lines which are continuously track-circuited and equipped with multiple-aspect colour light signals.

Track circuit operating clip — A safety device carried in driving cabs and guards' vans, which is placed on the track and, by short-circuiting the track circuit, places the signal in rear at red.

Tracker-ball — A means by which the signalman enters his commands and controls points and signals in an IECC.

Traffic moment — A measure of the combined quantity of road and rail traffic at a level crossing.

Trailing points — Points which cannot alter the direction of trains passing through them. When used in the opposite direction they become facing points.

Train describer — Apparatus used in modern signalboxes, which indicates to the signalman the location and identity of trains.

Train description (TD) — A four-character identity number carried by each train.

Train-operated route release (TORR) — A method of cancelling a route automatically after a train has passed over it.

Train Ready to Start plunger — A means by which station staff inform a signalman that a train is ready to depart.

Train Register Book — A book kept in signalboxes for recording the passage of trains, and other events.

Transponder — Equipment fixed between the rails which passes information electronically to a train passing over it.

Trap points — A switch blade or blades, which normally lie open to derail any vehicles which might otherwise escape from a goods line or sidings on to a passenger line.

Treadle — A mechanical or electronic device fixed to one of the rails for detecting the passage of a train over it.

Unbooked route — Not the route shown in the working timetable.

Up — A direction applied to a running line or train (see 'Down').

Visual display unit (VDU) — A screen on which various types of information can be displayed.

Warning board — A warning sign to a driver that he is approaching a temporary speed restriction.

'Welwyn' Control —A safety system applied to the operation of the block indicator.

Wire adjusters — Equipment in a signalbox for adjusting the tension in the wire operating a signal.

Wrong direction — A train movement in a direction which is opposite to the normal one.

Wrong-side failure —A failure of signalling equipment which does not place the protecting signal to danger (see 'Fail-safe').

Yellow aspect — Displayed by a colour light signal, and warns a driver to expect to find the next signal at red.